MY FIRST BILINGUAL ACTIVITY BOOK

ENGLISH-SPANISH WORKBOOK FOR KIDS 4-6 YEARS OLD

Alphabet Tracing, Number, Dot To Dot, Maze, Word Search And More!

Tabla de Contenidos

Nombre:.. Fecha:...

Alphabet Tracing/ Rastreo del Alfabeto

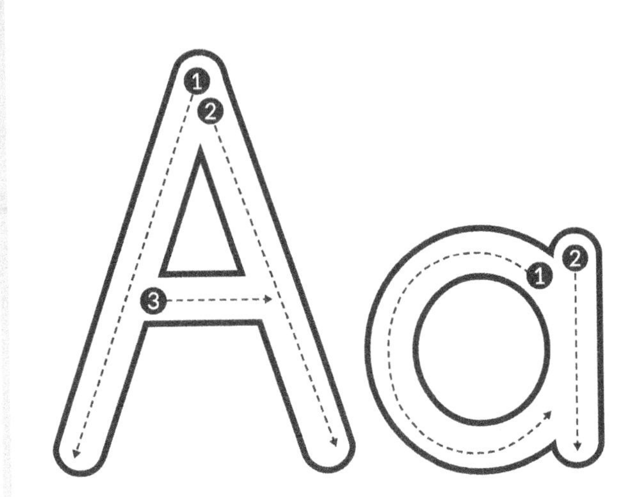

alce

moose

Trace the letter/Traza la letra.

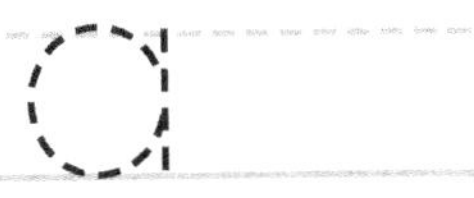

Write the letter/Escribe la letra.

A

a

Nombre:.. Fecha:...

Alphabet Tracing/
Rastreo del Alfabeto

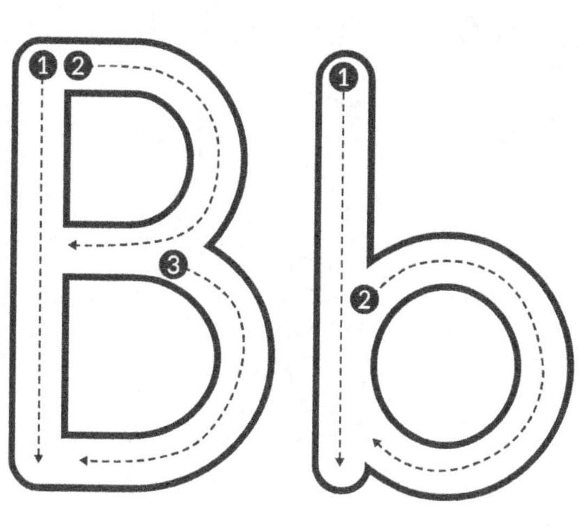

búho
owl

Trace the letter/Traza la letra.

B B B B B B

b b b b b b

Write the letter/Escribe la letra.

B

b

Nombre:.. Fecha:..

Alphabet Tracing/
Rastreo del Alfabeto

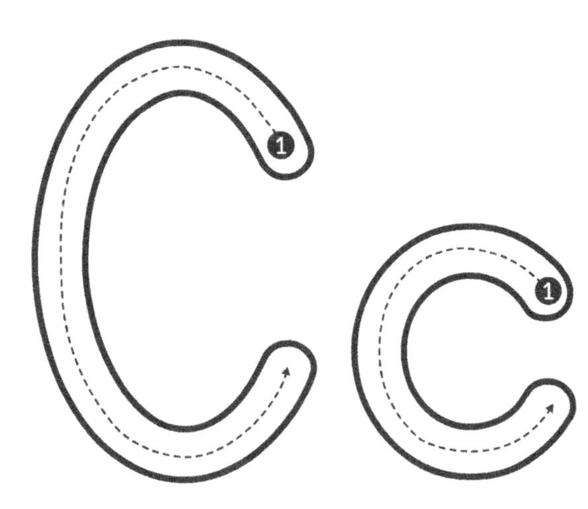

cabra
goat

Trace the letter/Traza la letra.

Write the letter/Escribe la letra.

C

c

Nombre:... Fecha:...

Alphabet Tracing/
Rastreo del Alfabeto

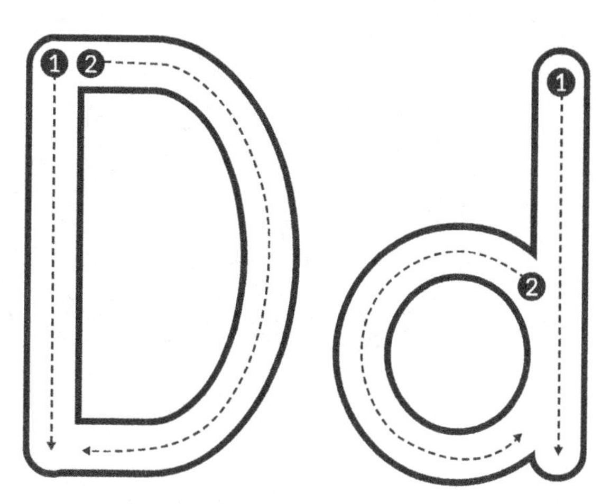

delfín
dolphin

Trace the letter/Traza la letra.

Write the letter/Escribe la letra.

D

d

Nombre:... Fecha:...

Alphabet Tracing/
Rastreo del Alfabeto

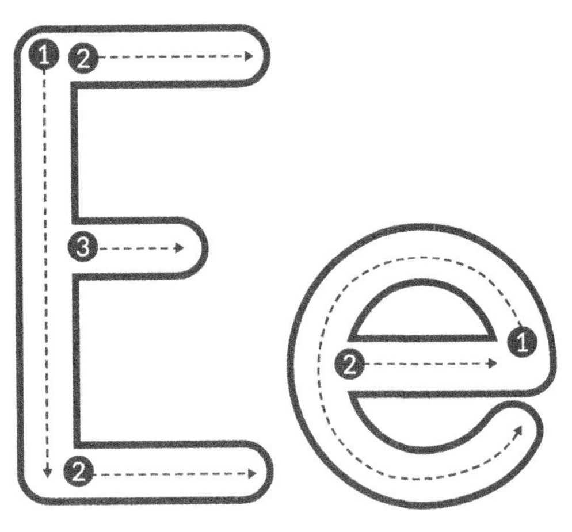

elefante

elephant

Trace the letter/Traza la letra.

Write the letter/Escribe la letra.

E

e

Nombre:.. Fecha:..

Alphabet Tracing/ Rastreo del Alfabeto

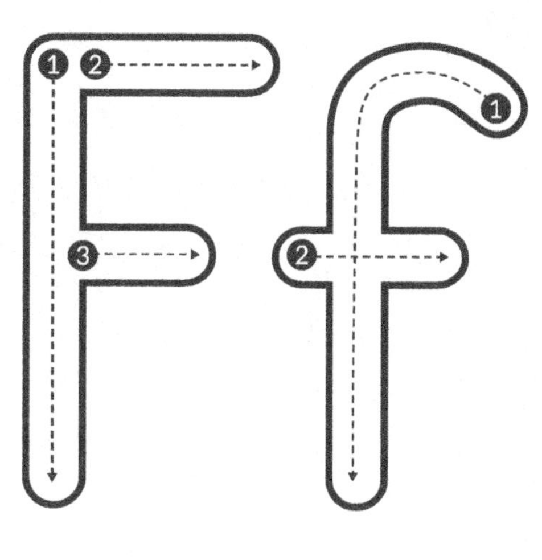

flamenco

flamingo

Trace the letter/Traza la letra.

Write the letter/Escribe la letra.

F

f

Nombre:.. Fecha:..

Alphabet Tracing/
Rastreo del Alfabeto

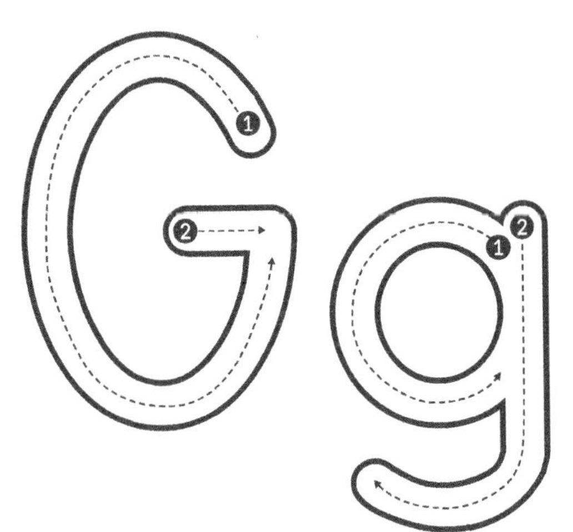

gallo

rooster

Trace the letter/Traza la letra.

Write the letter/Escribe la letra.

G

g

Nombre:... Fecha:...

Alphabet Tracing/
Rastreo del Alfabeto

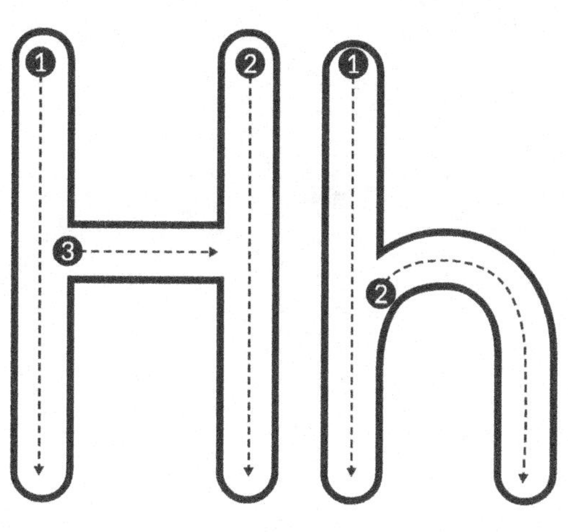

huevo

egg

Trace the letter/Traza la letra.

Write the letter/Escribe la letra.

H

h

Nombre:.. Fecha:..

Alphabet Tracing/
Rastreo del Alfabeto

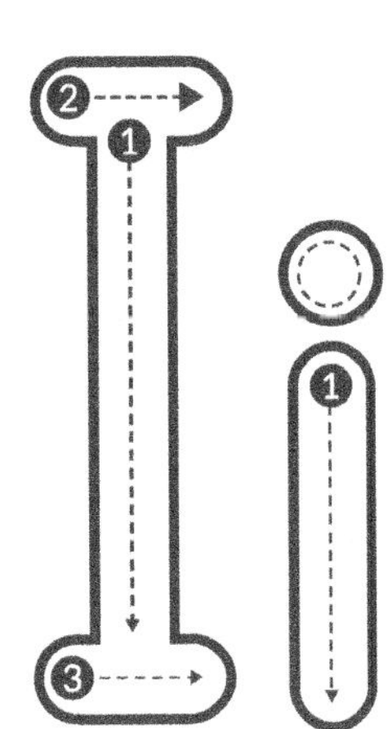

iguana

iguana

Trace the letter/Traza la letra.

Write the letter/Escribe la letra.

I

i

Nombre:.. Fecha:..

Alphabet Tracing/
Rastreo del Alfabeto

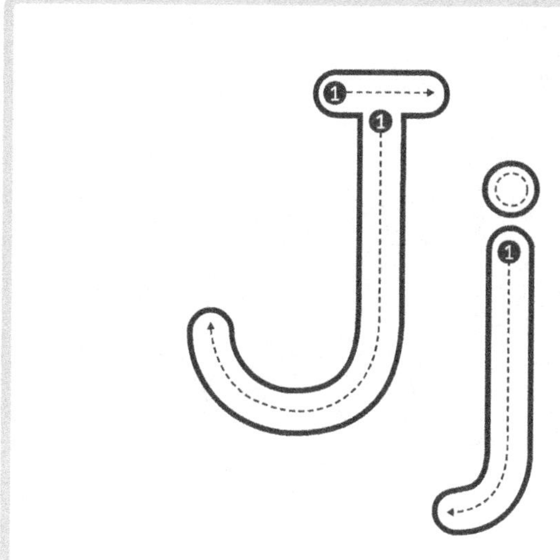

jugo
juice

Trace the letter/Traza la letra.

Write the letter/Escribe la letra.

J

j

Nombre:.. Fecha:..

Alphabet Tracing/
Rastreo del Alfabeto

koala
koala

Trace the letter/Traza la letra.

Write the letter/Escribe la letra.

K

k

Nombre:.. Fecha:..

Alphabet Tracing/
Rastreo del Alfabeto

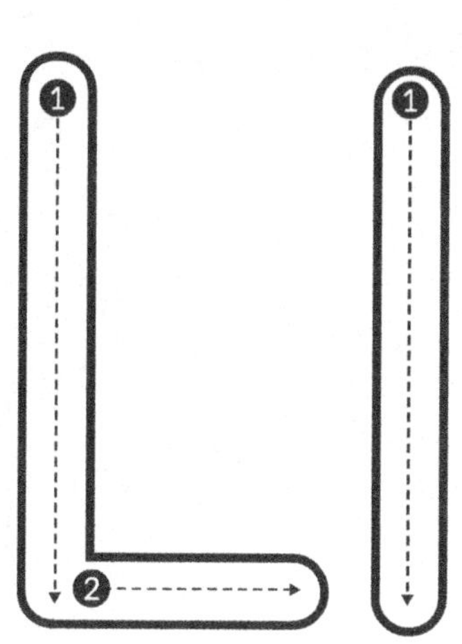

llama
llama

Trace the letter/Traza la letra.

Write the letter/Escribe la letra.

Nombre:.. Fecha:..

Alphabet Tracing/
Rastreo del Alfabeto

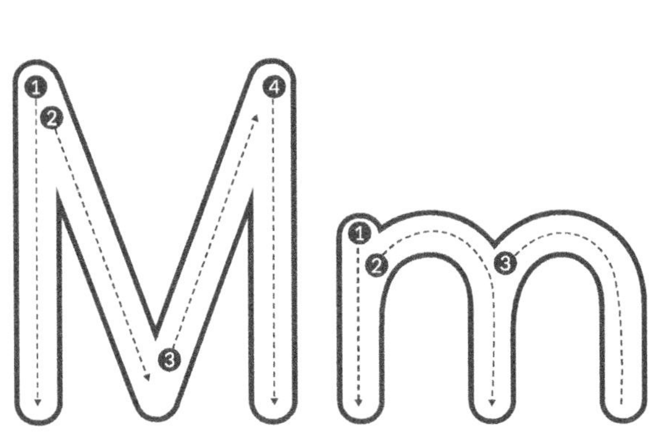

medusa

jellyfish

Trace the letter/Traza la letra.

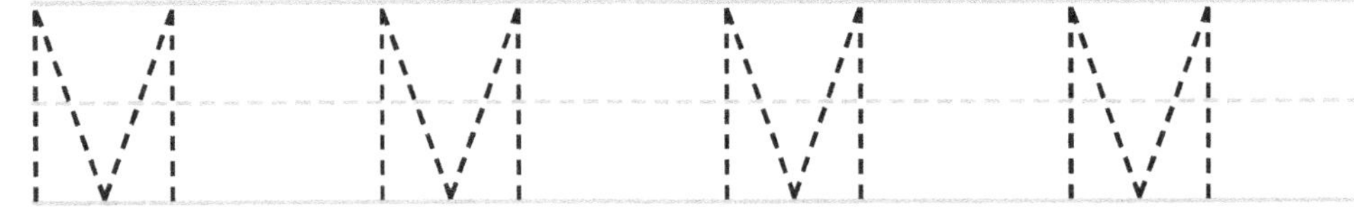

Write the letter/Escribe la letra.

Nombre:.. Fecha:..

Alphabet Tracing/
Rastreo del Alfabeto

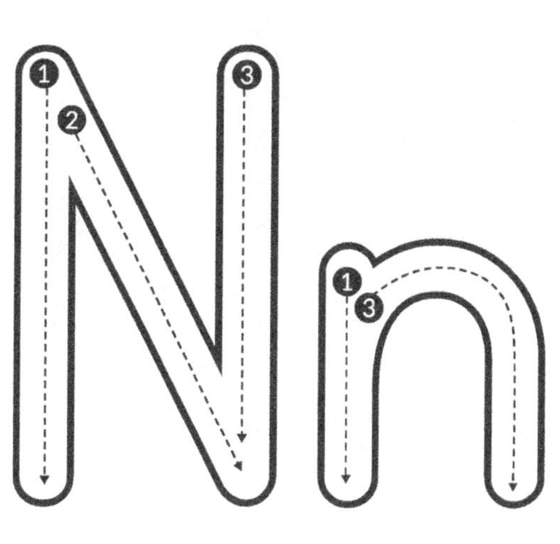

numbat
numbat

Trace the letter/Traza la letra.

Write the letter/Escribe la letra.

Nombre:.. Fecha:..

Alphabet Tracing/
Rastreo del Alfabeto

ñandú
rhea

Trace the letter/Traza la letra.

Write the letter/Escribe la letra.

Nombre:.. Fecha:..

Alphabet Tracing/ Rastreo del Alfabeto

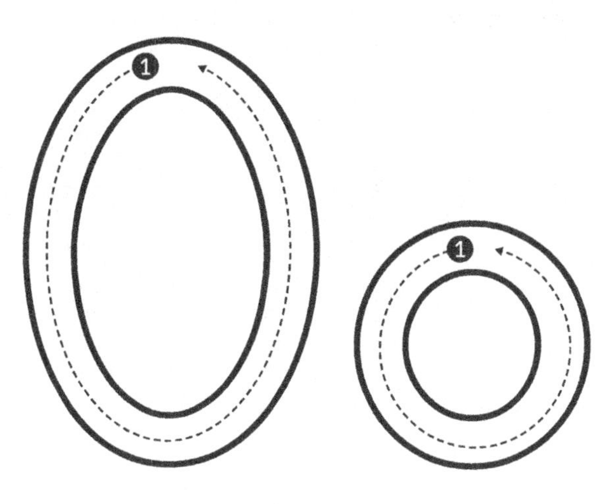

oso
bear

Trace the letter/Traza la letra.

Write the letter/Escribe la letra.

Nombre:.. Fecha:..

Alphabet Tracing/
Rastreo del Alfabeto

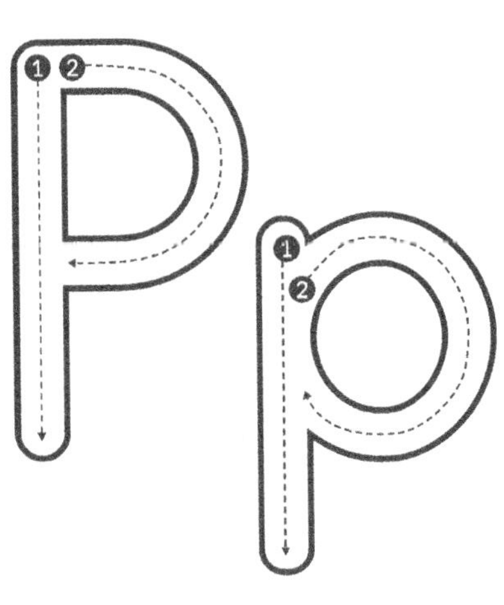

panda
panda

Trace the letter/Traza la letra.

P P P P P P

p p p p p p

Write the letter/Escribe la letra.

P

p

Nombre:.. Fecha:..

Alphabet Tracing/
Rastreo del Alfabeto

queso
cheese

Trace the letter/Traza la letra.

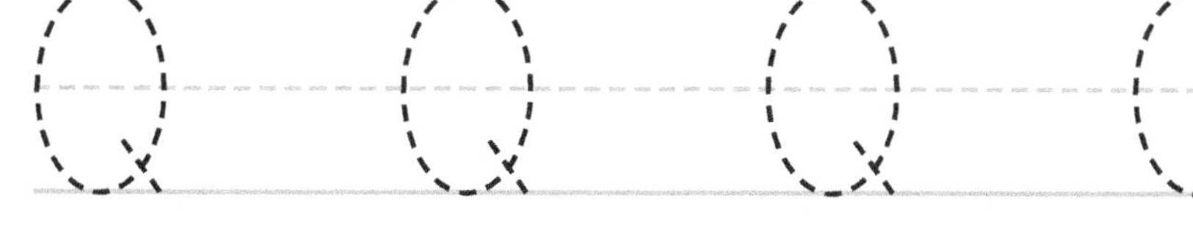

Write the letter/Escribe la letra.

Nombre:.. Fecha:..

Alphabet Tracing/
Rastreo del Alfabeto

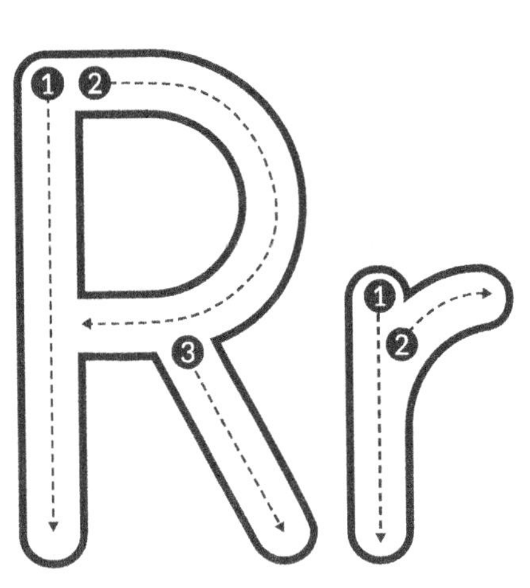

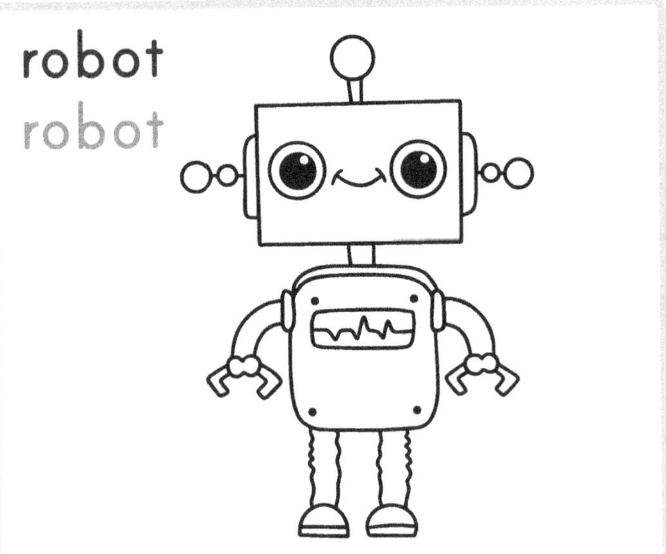

Trace the letter/Traza la letra.

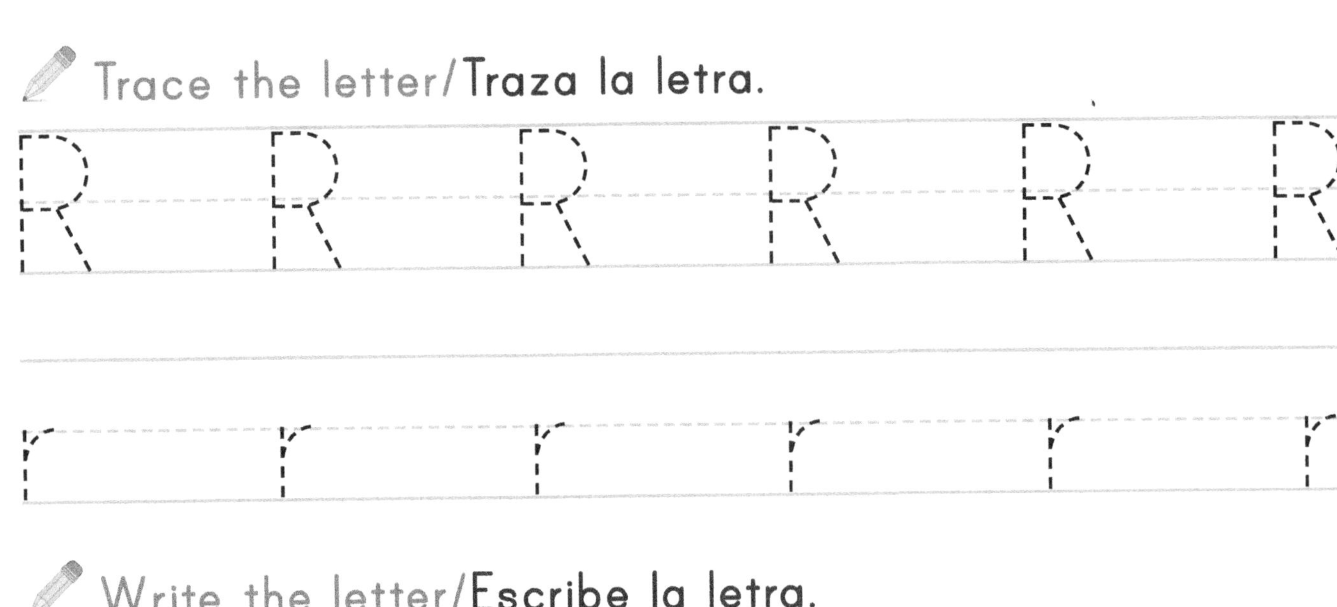

Write the letter/Escribe la letra.

R

r

Nombre:.. Fecha:..

Alphabet Tracing/
Rastreo del Alfabeto

sandia
watermelon

Trace the letter/Traza la letra.

Write the letter/Escribe la letra.

Nombre:.. Fecha:..

Alphabet Tracing/
Rastreo del Alfabeto

T t

tiburón
shark

Trace the letter/Traza la letra.

Write the letter/Escribe la letra.

T

t

Nombre:.. Fecha:..

Alphabet Tracing/
Rastreo del Alfabeto

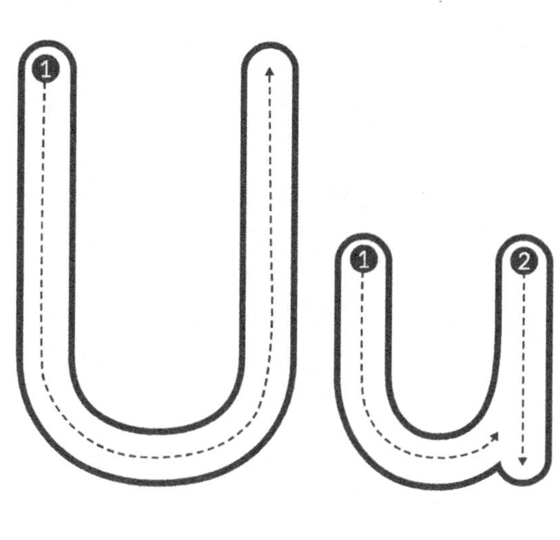

urial

urial

Trace the letter/Traza la letra.

Write the letter/Escribe la letra.

U

u

Nombre:... Fecha:...

Alphabet Tracing/
Rastreo del Alfabeto

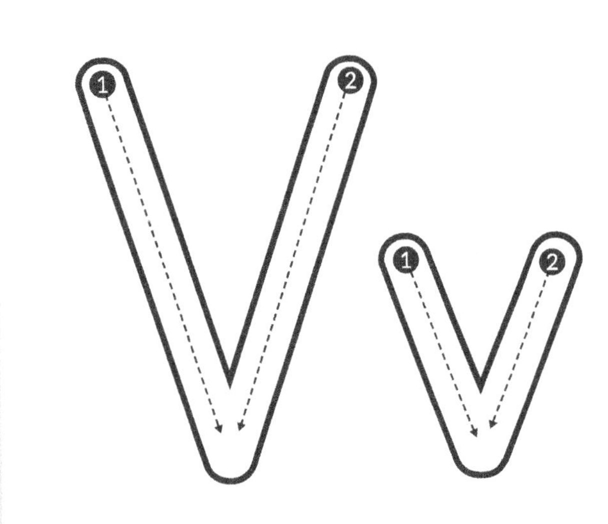

vaca

cow

Trace the letter/Traza la letra.

V V V V V V

v v v v v v

Write the letter/Escribe la letra.

V

v

Nombre:.. Fecha:..

Alphabet Tracing/
Rastreo del Alfabeto

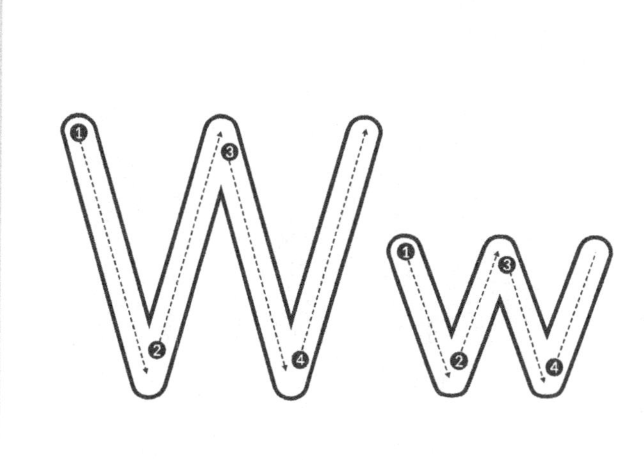

Trace the letter/**Traza la letra.**

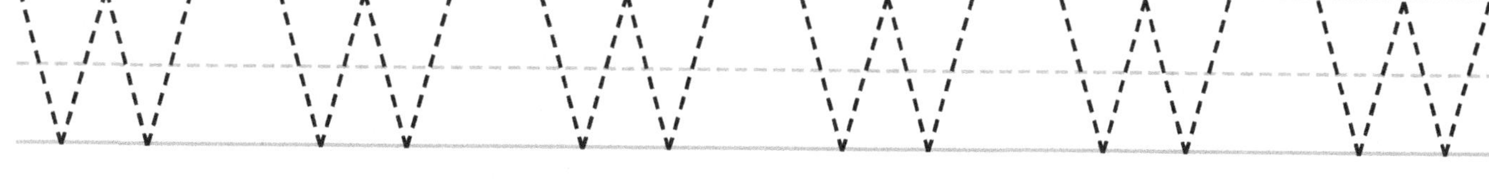

Write the letter/**Escribe la letra.**

W

Nombre:.. Fecha:..

Alphabet Tracing/
Rastreo del Alfabeto

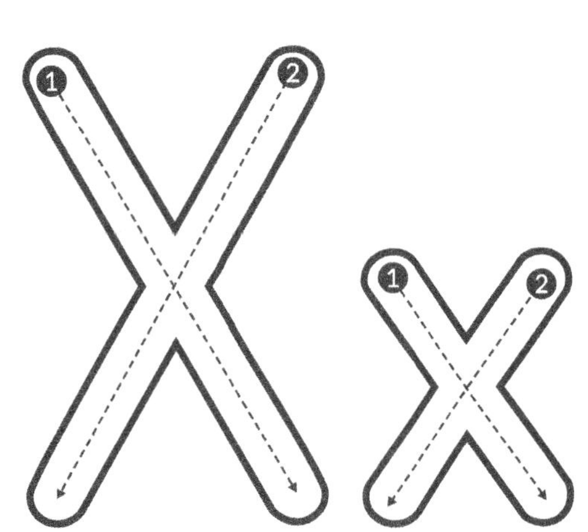

xerus

xerus

Trace the letter/Traza la letra.

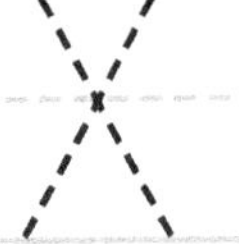

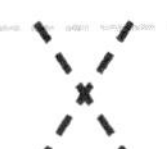

Write the letter/Escribe la letra.

Nombre:.. Fecha:..

Alphabet Tracing/
Rastreo del Alfabeto

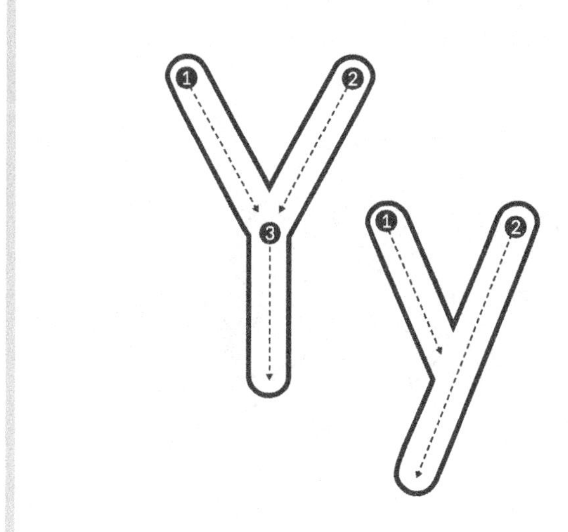

Trace the letter/Traza la letra.

Y Y Y Y Y Y

y y y y y y

Write the letter/Escribe la letra.

Y

y

Nombre:.. Fecha:..

Alphabet Tracing/
Rastreo del Alfabeto

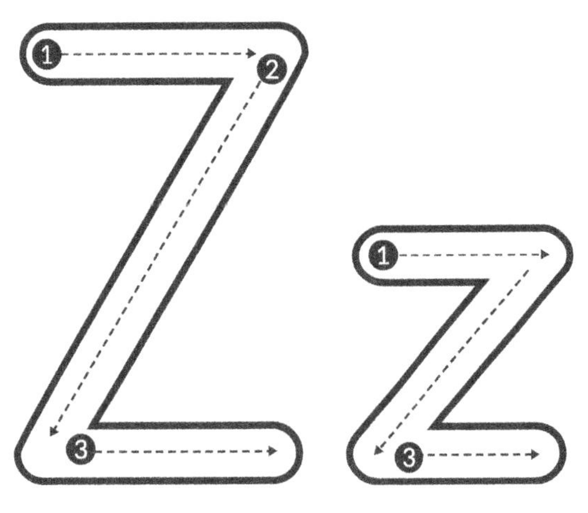

zapato

shoe

Trace the letter/Traza la letra.

Write the letter/Escribe la letra.

Z

z

Nombre:.. Fecha:..

A-Z Uppercase Letters/
Letras Mayúsculas de la A a la Z

A B C D

E F G H

I J K L

M N Ñ O

P Q R S

T U V W

X Y Z

Nombre:.. Fecha:..

a-z Lowercase Letters/
Letras Minúsculas a-z

a b c d

e f g h

i j k l

m n ñ o

p q r s

t u v w

x y z

Nombre:... Fecha:...

Letter Recognition/
Reconocimiento de Letras

Color the boxes that have uppercase letters in red and color the boxes that have lower case letters in green/
Colorea los cuadros con mayúsculas de rojo y los cuadros con minúsculas de verde.

G	a	H	J	I
b	F	e	A	d
c	g	f	h	i
j	l	B	C	E
k	D	n	o	Z
Y	m	X	w	W
r	V	t	U	s
A	v	T	u	S
w	Q	s	z	R
O	P	x	M	y

Nombre:.. Fecha:..

Letter Recognition/
Reconocimiento de Letras

Color the boxes that have uppercase letters in red and color the boxes that have lower case letters in green/
Colorea los cuadros con mayúsculas de rojo y los cuadros con minúsculas de verde.

g	A	h	j	i
B	f	E	a	D
C	G	F	H	I
J	L	b	c	e
K	d	N	O	z
y	M	x	W	w
R	v	T	u	S
a	V	t	U	s
W	q	S	Z	r
o	p	X	m	Y

Nombre:.. Fecha:..

Word to Picture Matching/
Coincidencia de Palabra e Imagen

Draw a line to match the picture on the left to the word on the right/
Dibuja una línea para unir la imagen de la izquierda con la palabra de la derecha.

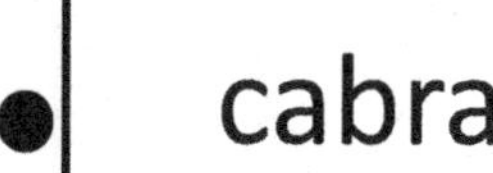

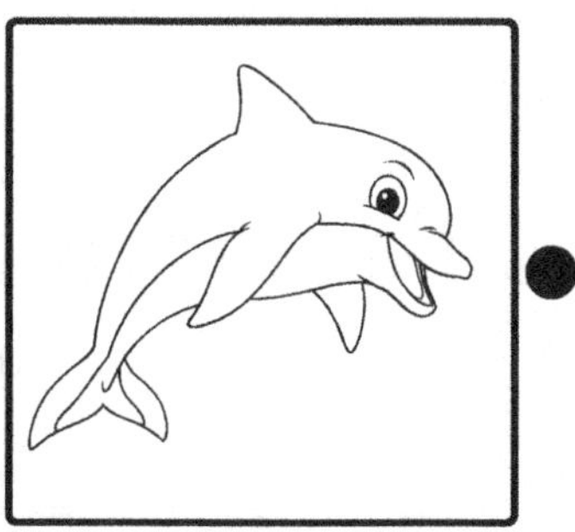

elefante

búho

Nombre:.. Fecha:..

Word to Picture Matching/
Coincidencia de Palabra e Imagen

Draw a line to match the picture on the left to the word on the right/
Dibuja una línea para unir la imagen de la izquierda con la palabra de la derecha.

huevo

iguana

jugo

flamenco

gallo

Nombre:.. Fecha:...

Word to Picture Matching/
Coincidencia de Palabra e Imagen

Draw a line to match the picture on the left to the word on the right/
Dibuja una línea para unir la imagen de la izquierda con la palabra de la derecha.

oso

medusa

numbat

Nombre:.. Fecha:..

Word to Picture Matching/
Coincidencia de Palabra e Imagen

Draw a line to match the picture on the left to the word on the right/
Dibuja una línea para unir la imagen de la izquierda con la palabra de la derecha.

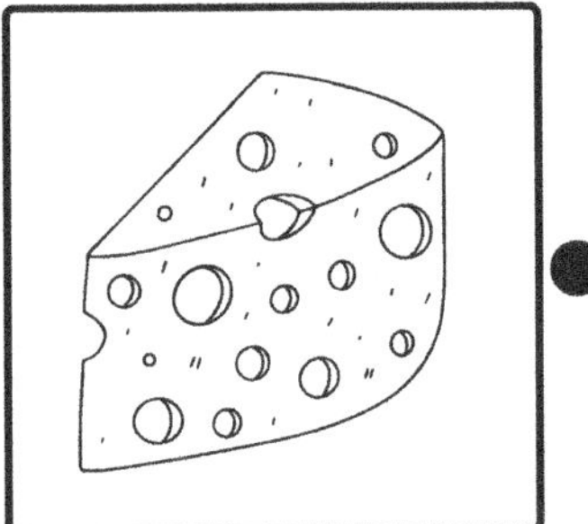

queso

robot

sandia

Nombre:.. Fecha:..

Word to Picture Matching/
Coincidencia de Palabra e Imagen

Draw a line to match the picture on the left to the word on the right/
Dibuja una línea para unir la imagen de la izquierda con la palabra de la derecha.

vaca

urial

wasabi

yak

xerus

Nombre:.. Fecha:..

Number Tracing/
Rastreo de Números

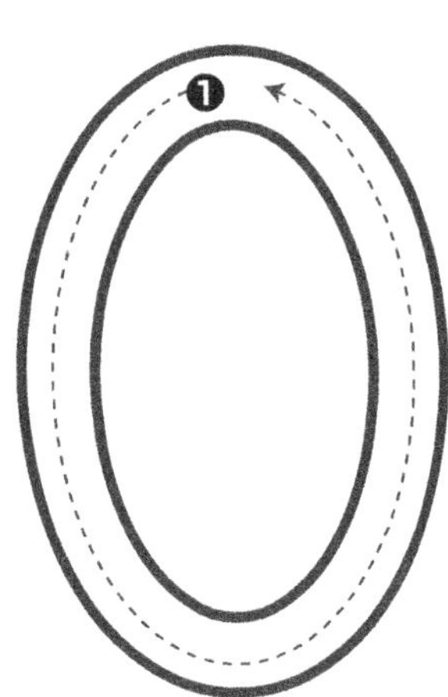

Trace the number/Rastrea el número.

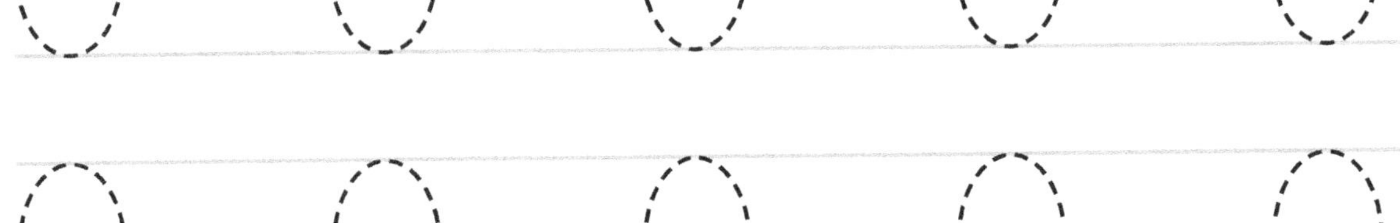

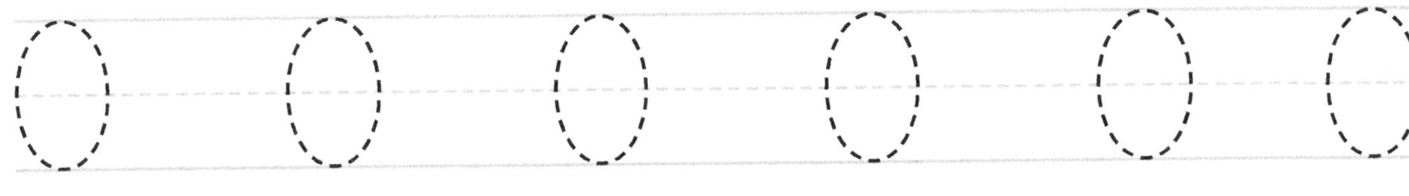

Trace the number word/Traza la palabra numérica.

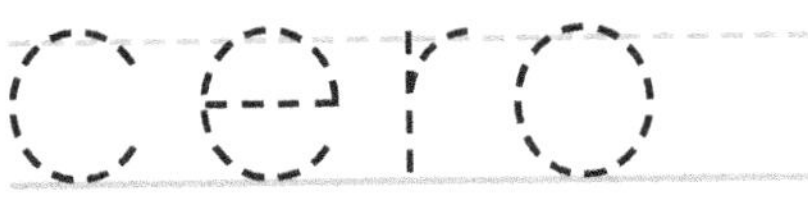

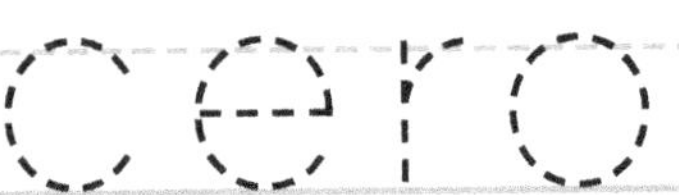

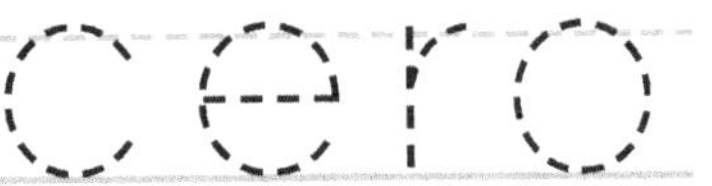

Nombre:.. Fecha:..

Number Tracing/ Rastreo de Números

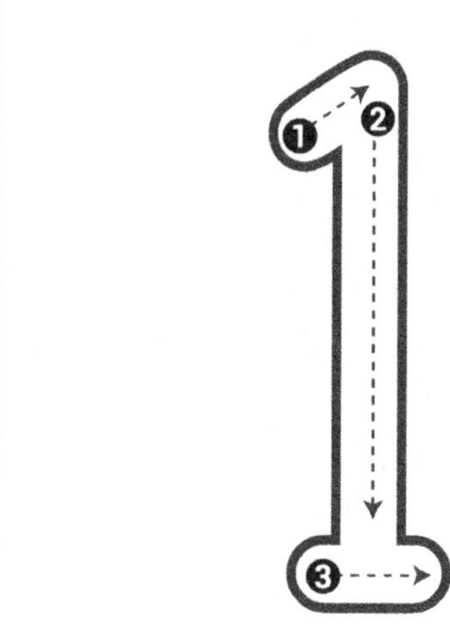

Trace the number/Rastrea el número.

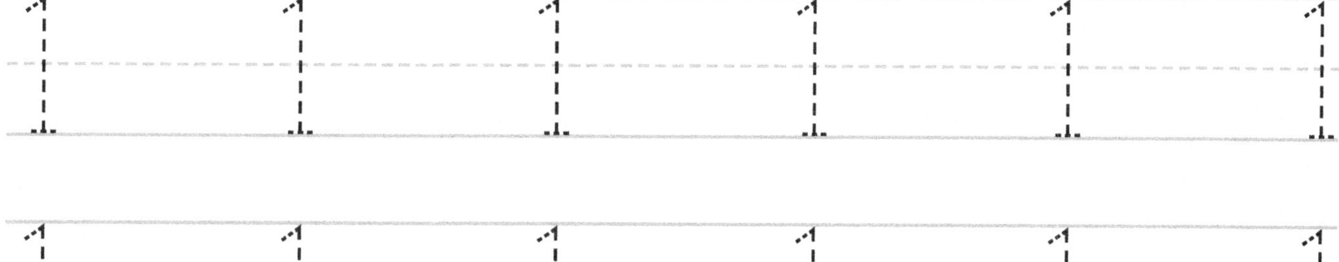

Trace the number word/Traza la palabra numérica.

one one one one

uno uno uno uno

Nombre:.. Fecha:..

Number Tracing/
Rastreo de Números

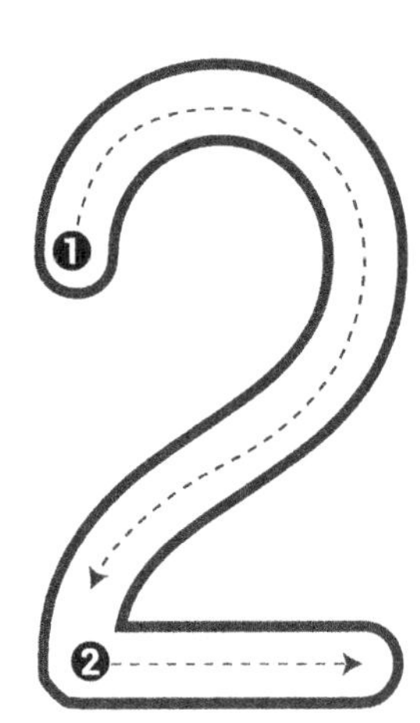

Trace the number/Rastrea el número.

Trace the number word/Traza la palabra numérica.

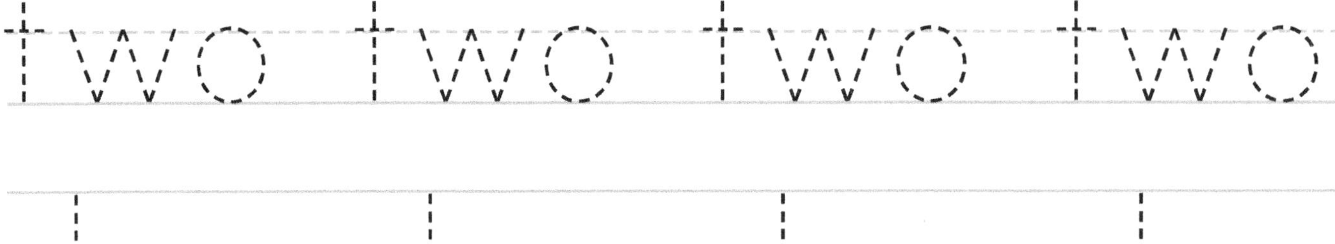

Nombre:.. Fecha:..

Number Tracing/
Rastreo de Números

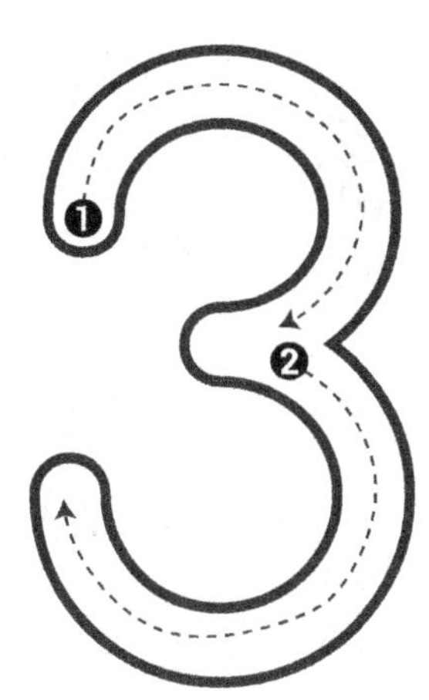

Trace the number/**Rastrea el número.**

  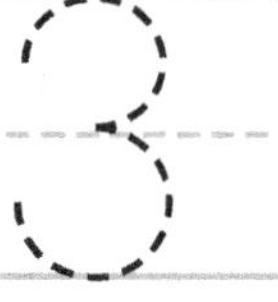 

  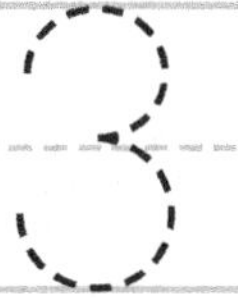 

Trace the number word/**Traza la palabra numérica.**

three three three

tres tres tres tres

Nombre:.. Fecha:..

Number Tracing/
Rastreo de Números

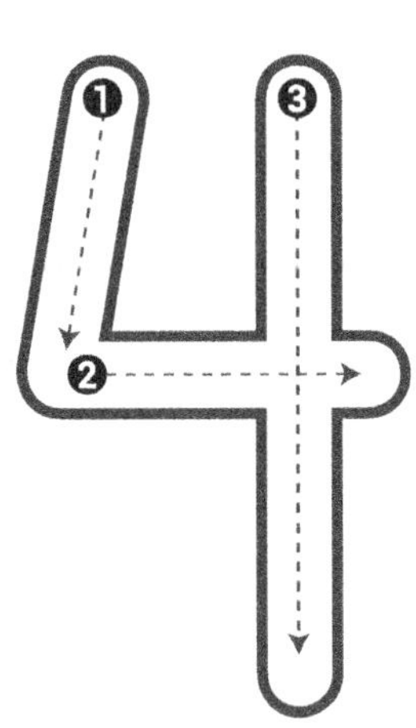

Trace the number/Rastrea el número.

4 4 4 4 4 4

4 4 4 4 4 4

Trace the number word/Traza la palabra numérica.

four four four four

cuatro cuatro cuatro

Nombre:.. Fecha:..

Number Tracing/
Rastreo de Números

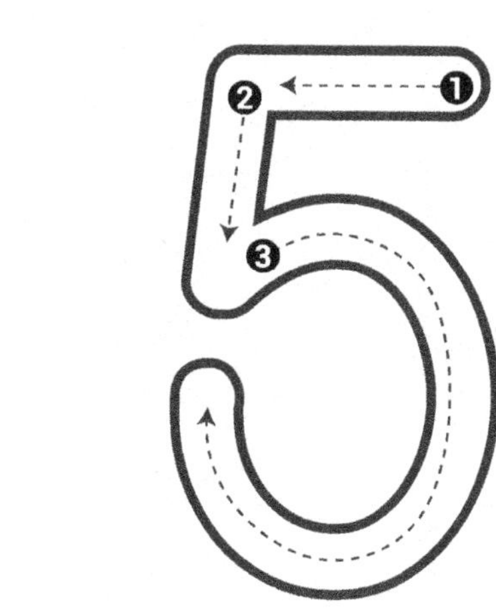

Trace the number/**Rastrea el número.**

5 5 5 5 5 5

5 5 5 5 5 5

Trace the number word/**Traza la palabra numérica.**

five five five five

cinco cinco cinco

Nombre:.. Fecha:..

Number Tracing/
Rastreo de Números

Trace the number/Rastrea el número.

6 6 6 6 6 6

6 6 6 6 6 6

Trace the number word/Traza la palabra numérica.

six six six six six

seis seis seis seis

Nombre:.. Fecha:..

Number Tracing/
Rastreo de Números

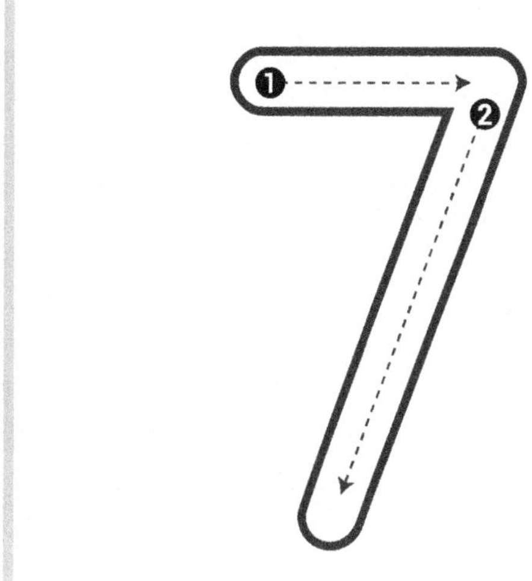

Trace the number/**Rastrea el número.**

7 7 7 7 7 7

7 7 7 7 7 7

Trace the number word/**Traza la palabra numérica.**

seven seven seven

siete siete siete

Nombre:.. Fecha:..

Number Tracing/
Rastreo de Números

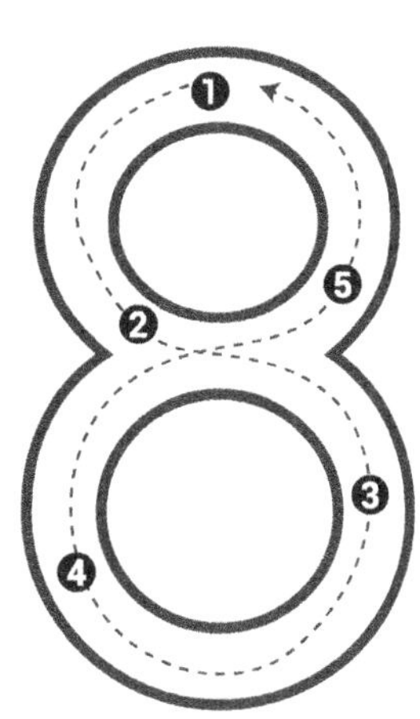

Trace the number/**Rastrea el número.**

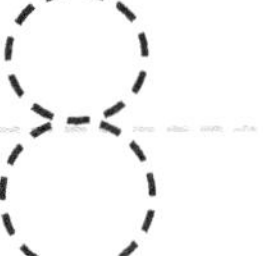 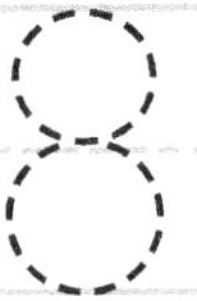 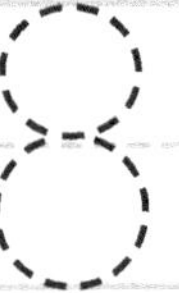 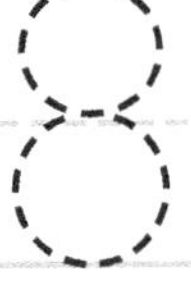  

 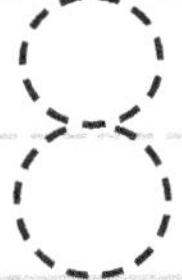 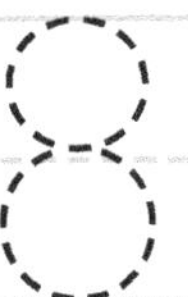 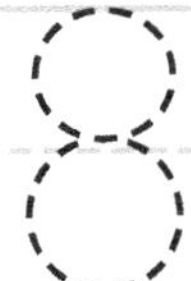  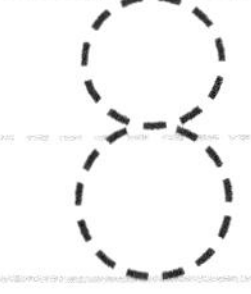

Trace the number word/**Traza la palabra numérica.**

  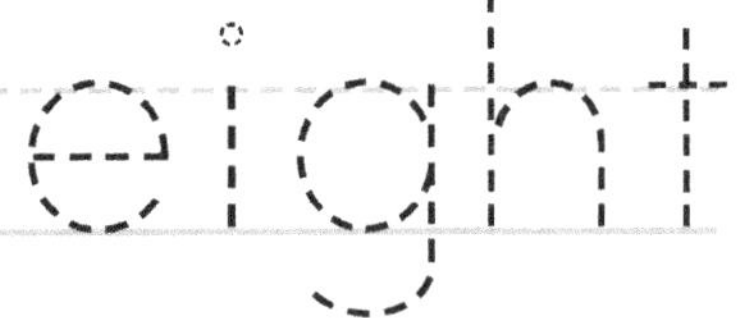

  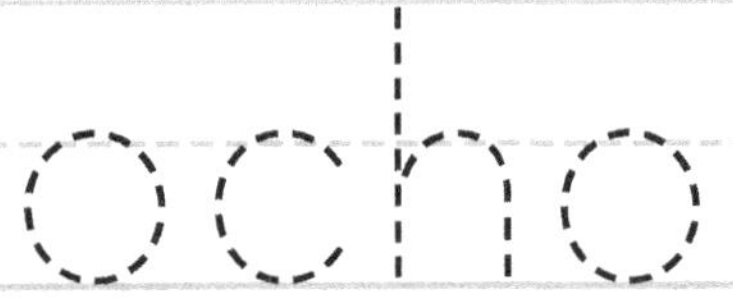

Nombre:... Fecha:...

Number Tracing/
Rastreo de Números

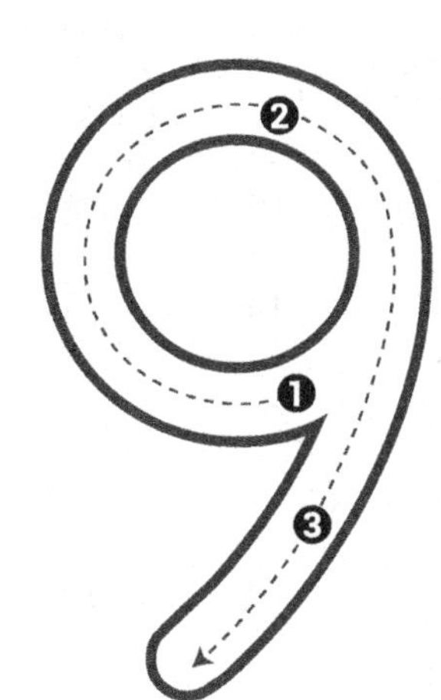

Trace the number/Rastrea el número.

Trace the number word/Traza la palabra numérica.

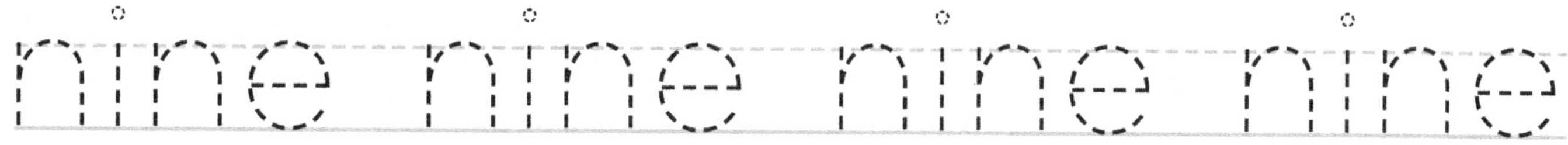

Nombre:.. Fecha:..

Number Tracing/ Rastreo de Números

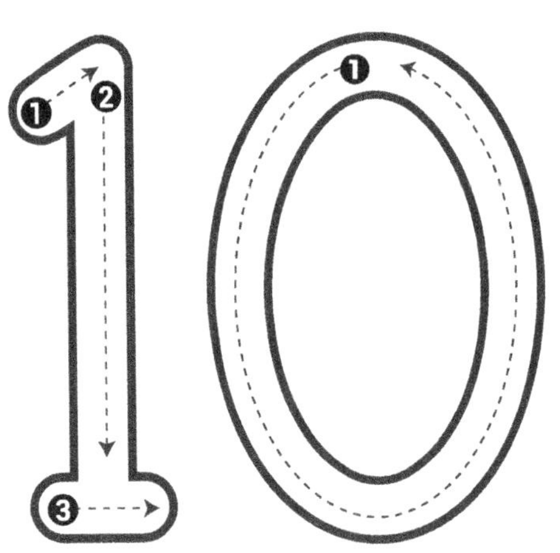

Trace the number/Rastrea el número.

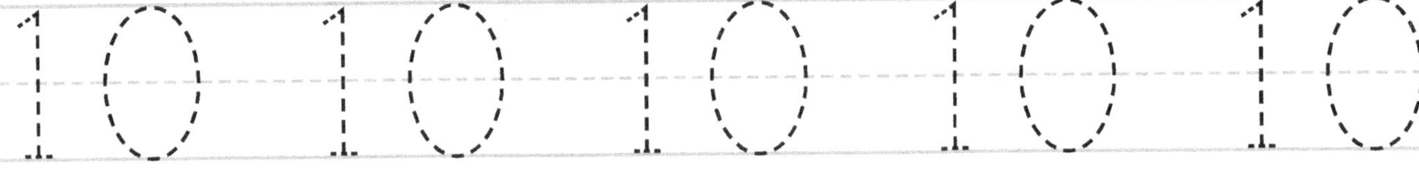

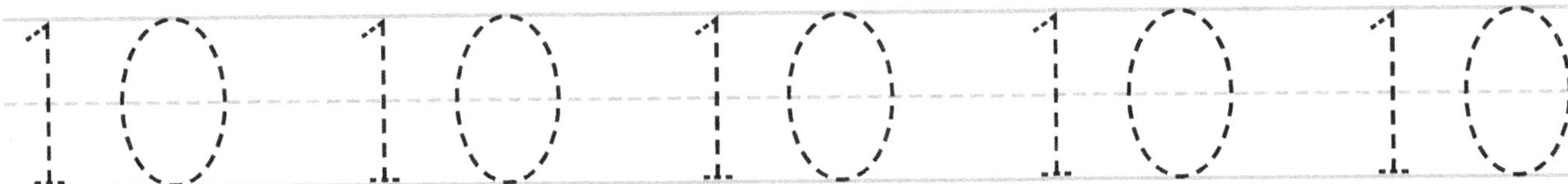

Trace the number word/Traza la palabra numérica.

ten ten ten ten ten

Nombre:.. Fecha:..

Number Tracing/
Rastreo de Números

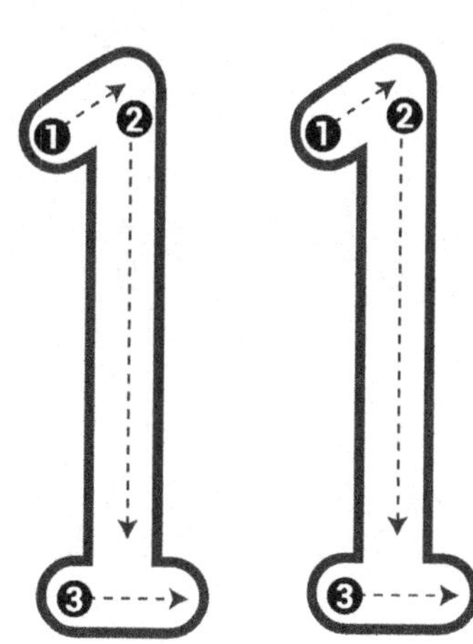

Trace the number/Rastrea el número.

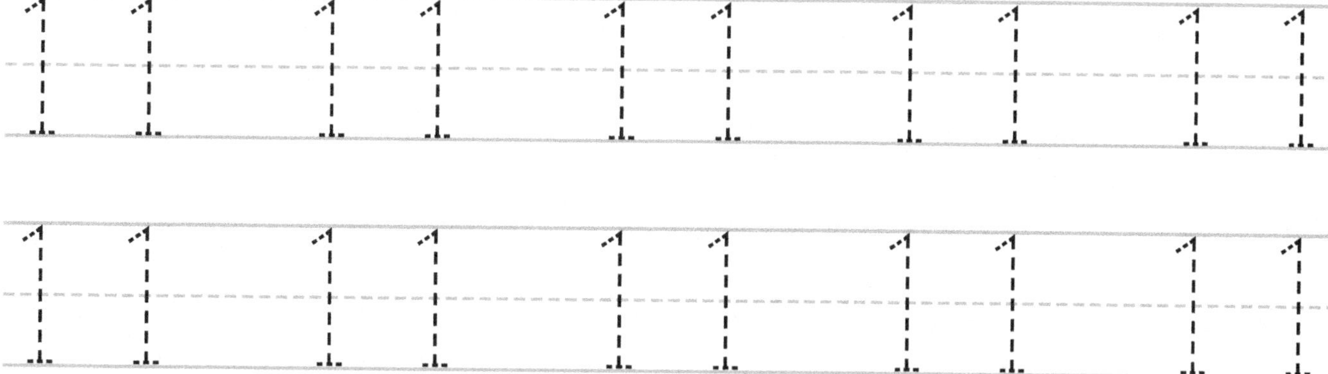

Trace the number word/Traza la palabra numérica.

Nombre:... Fecha:...

Number Tracing/ Rastreo de Números

Trace the number/Rastrea el número.

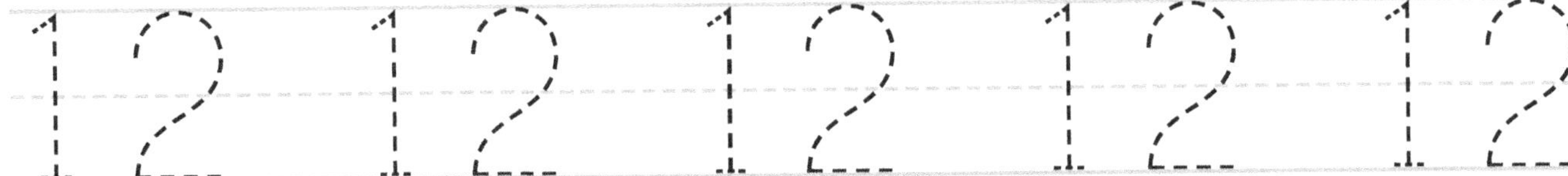

Trace the number word/Traza la palabra numérica.

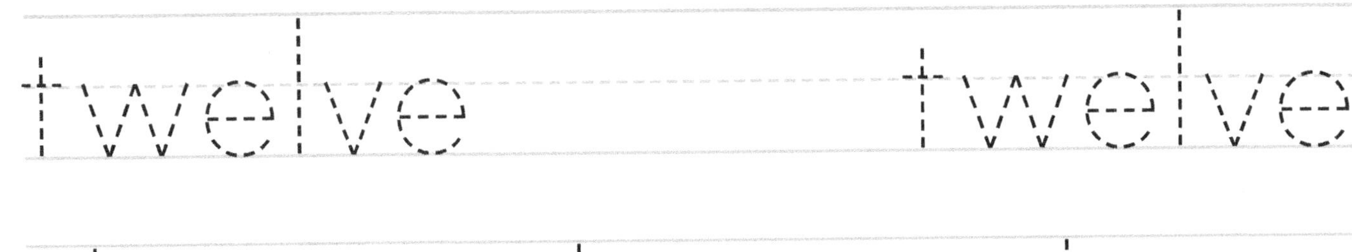

Nombre:.. Fecha:..

Number Tracing/
Rastreo de Números

Trace the number/Rastrea el número.

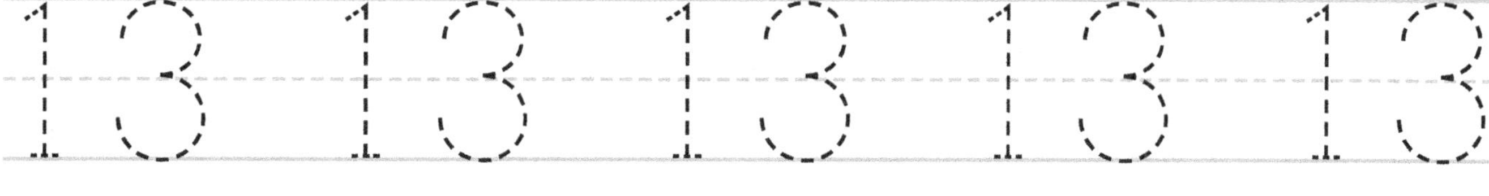

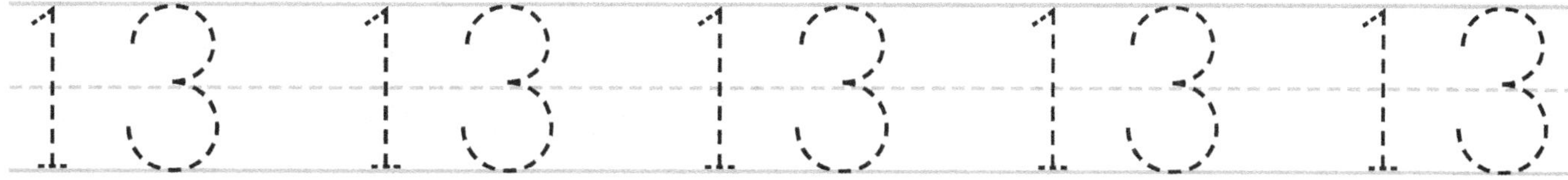

Trace the number word/Traza la palabra numérica.

thirteen thirteen

Nombre:.. Fecha:..

Number Tracing/
Rastreo de Números

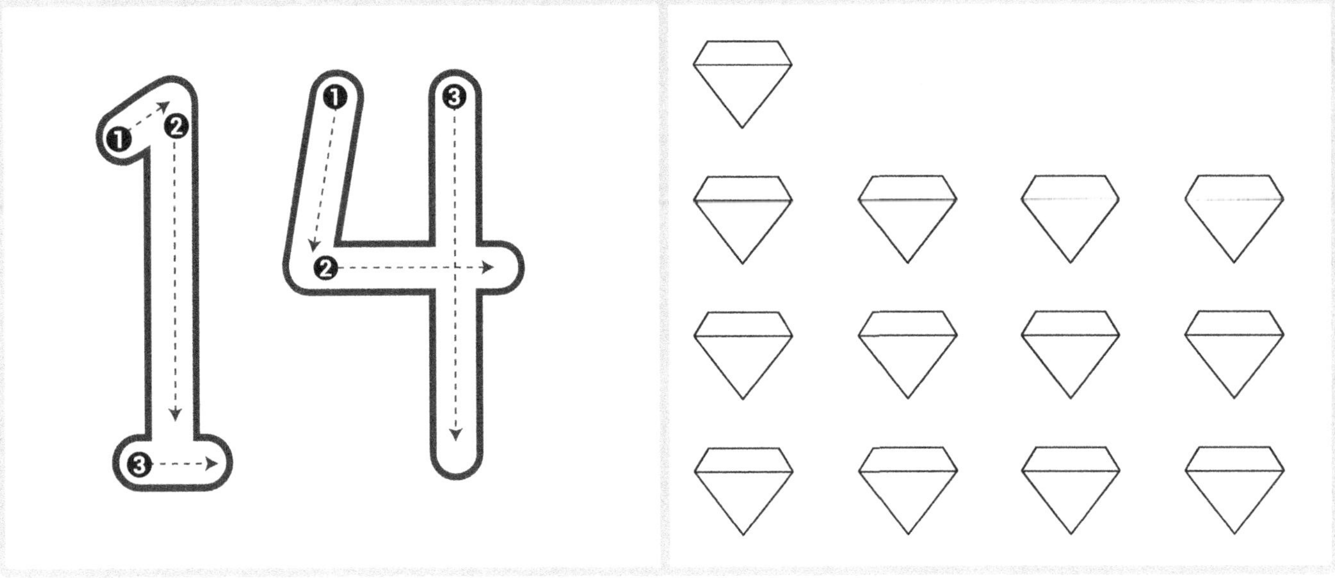

Trace the number/Rastrea el número.

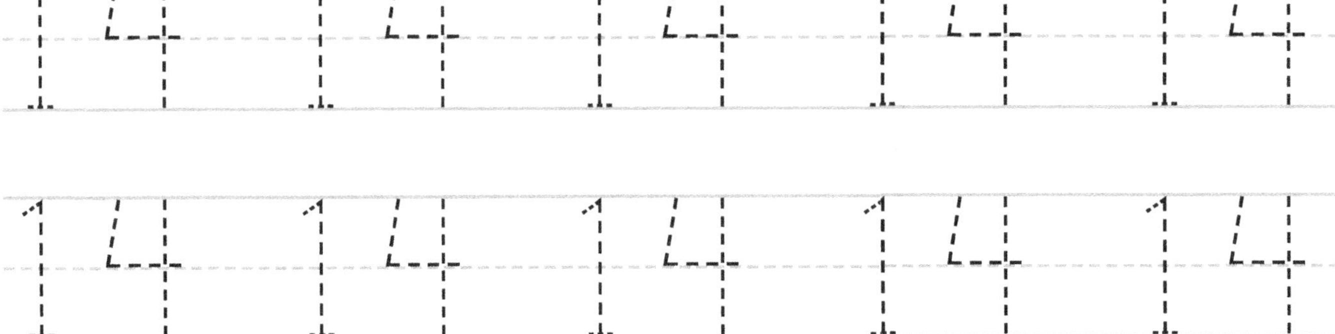

Trace the number word/Traza la palabra numérica.

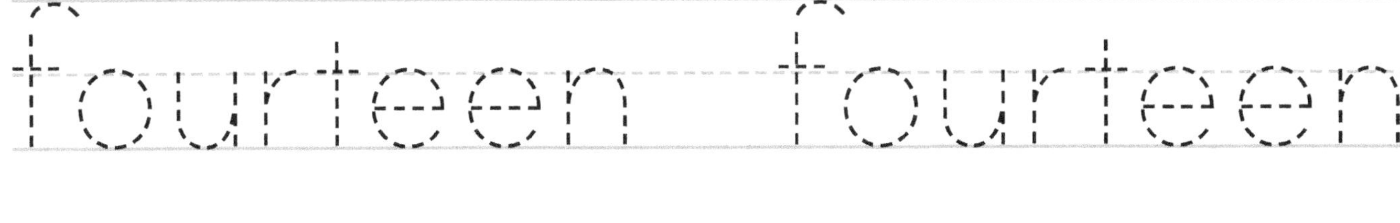

Nombre:.. Fecha:..

Number Tracing/
Rastreo de Números

Trace the number/Rastrea el número.

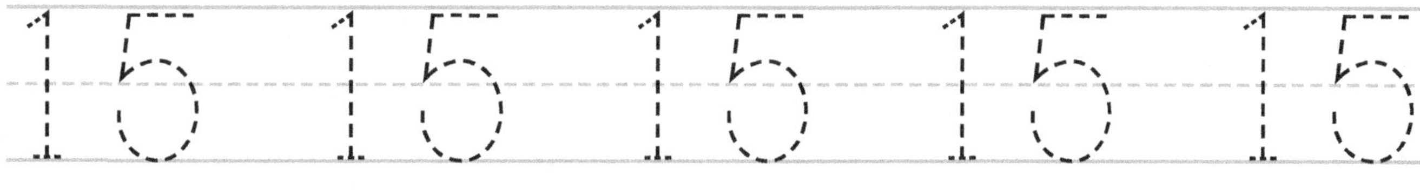

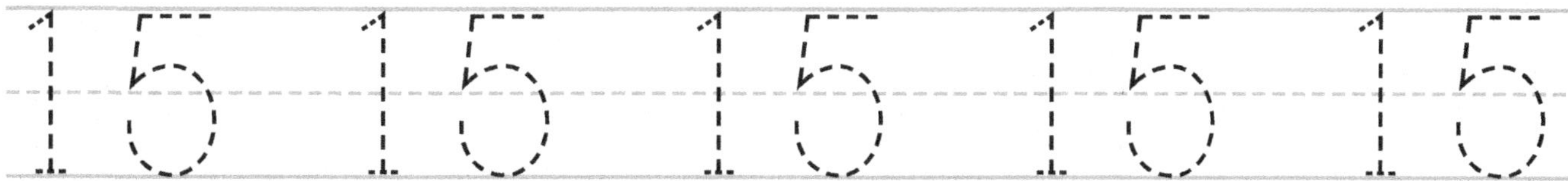

Trace the number word/Traza la palabra numérica.

fifteen fifteen

quince quince quince

Nombre:.. Fecha:..

Number Tracing/
Rastreo de Números

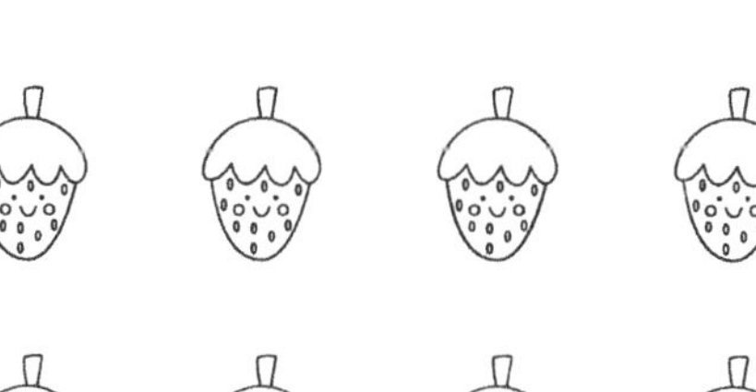

Trace the number/**Rastrea el número.**

16 16 16 16 16

16 16 16 16 16

Trace the number word/**Traza la palabra numérica.**

sixteen sixteen

dieciséis dieciséis

Nombre:... Fecha:...

Number Tracing/
Rastreo de Números

Trace the number/Rastrea el número.

17 17 17 17 17

17 17 17 17 17

Trace the number word/Traza la palabra numérica.

seventeen

diecisiete diecisiete

Nombre:.. Fecha:..

Number Tracing/ Rastreo de Números

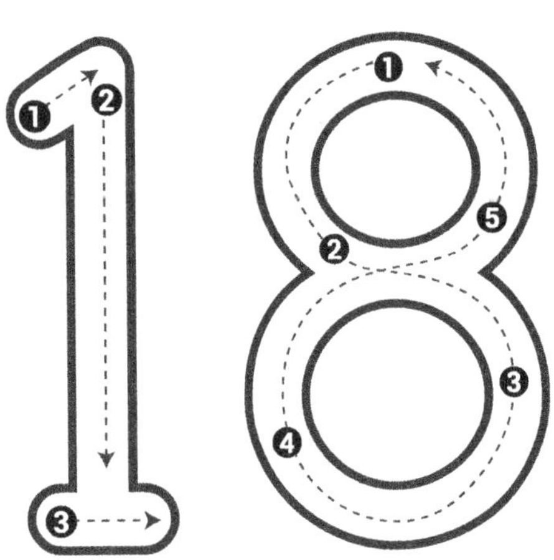

Trace the number/Rastrea el número.

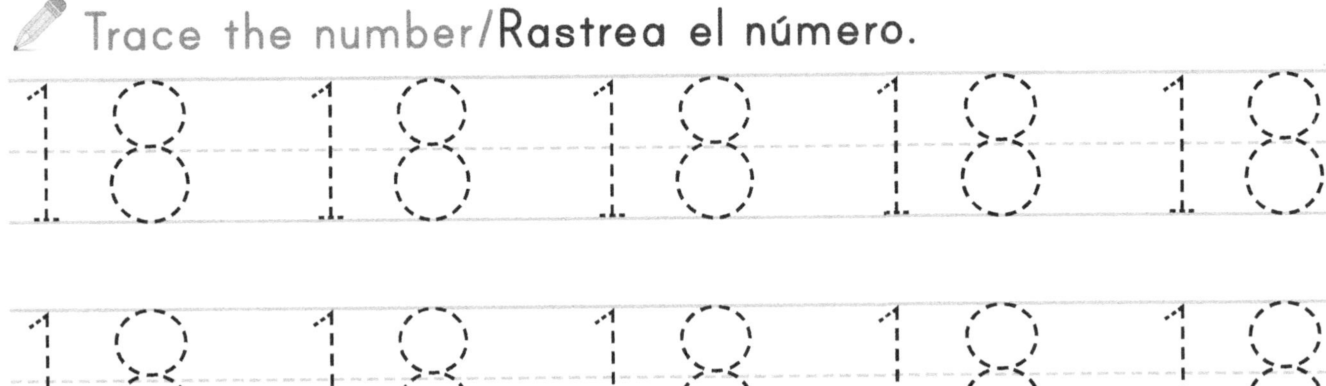

Trace the number word/Traza la palabra numérica.

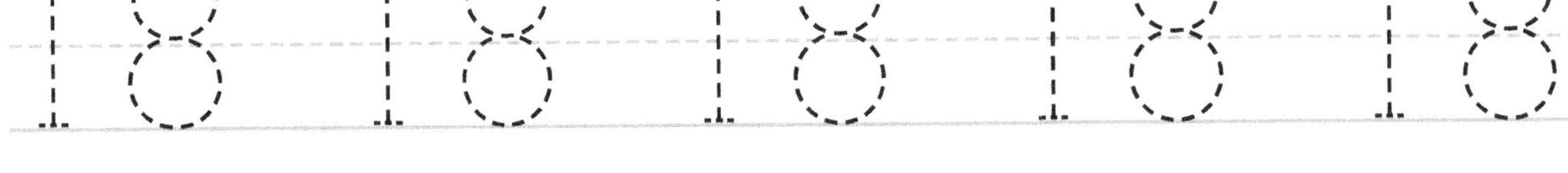

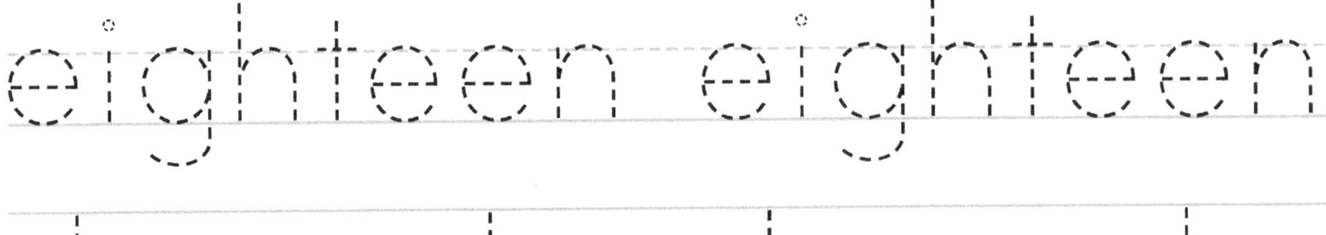

Nombre:.. Fecha:..

Number Tracing/
Rastreo de Números

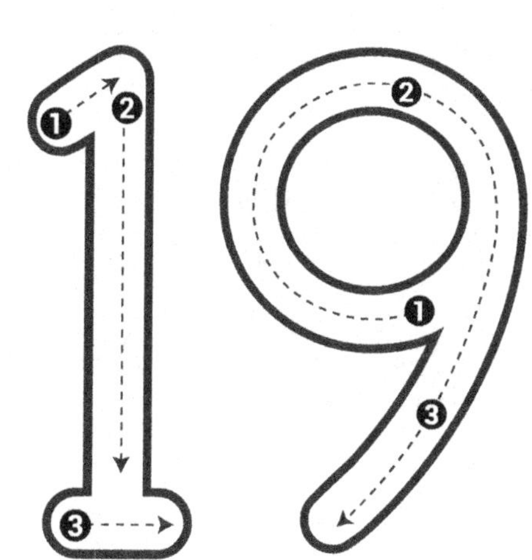

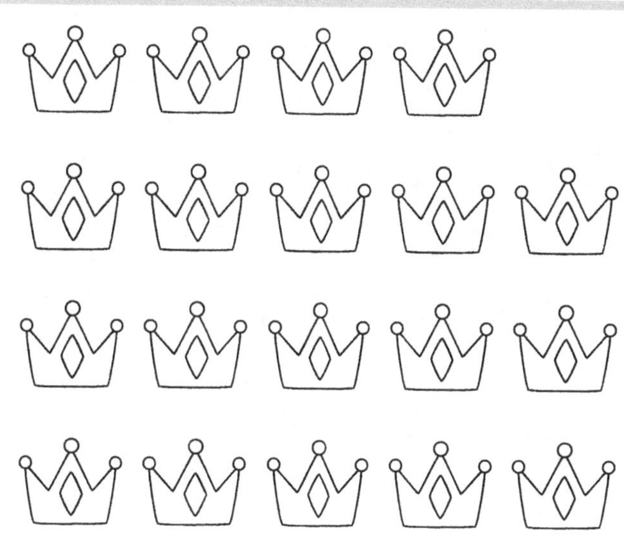

Trace the number/Rastrea el número.

19 19 19 19 19

19 19 19 19 19

Trace the number word/Traza la palabra numérica.

nineteen nineteen

diecinueve diecinueve

Nombre:... Fecha:...

Number Tracing/
Rastreo de Números

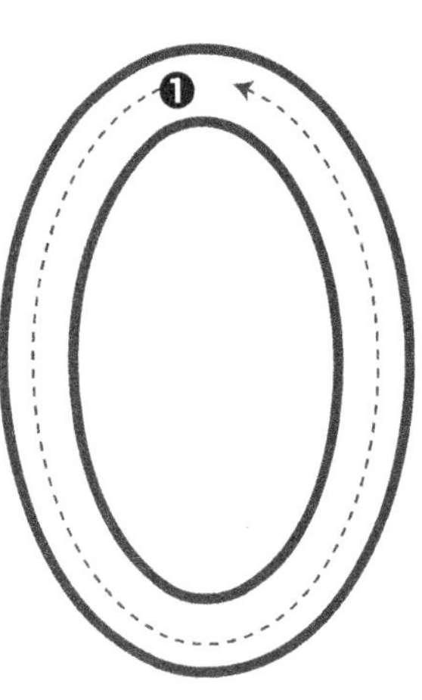

Trace the number/Rastrea el número.

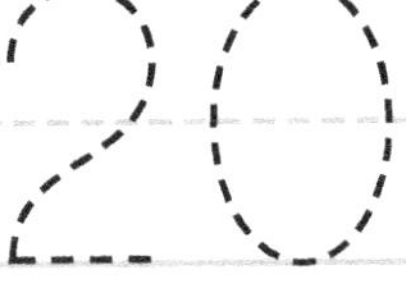
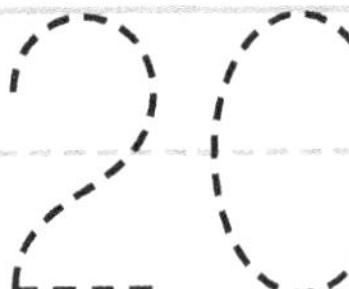

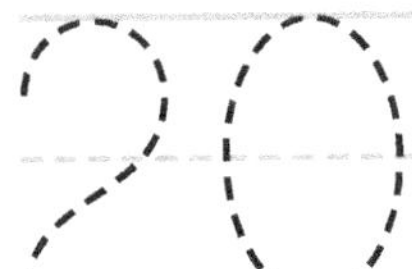
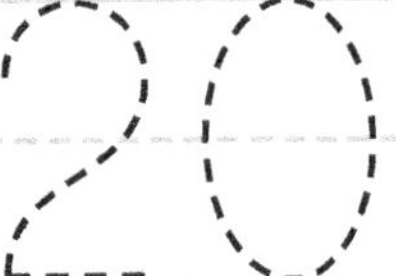
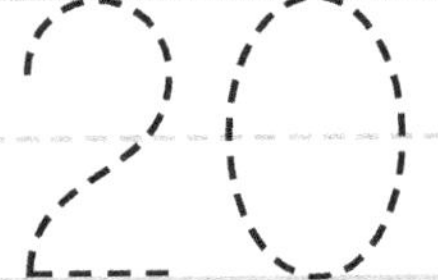

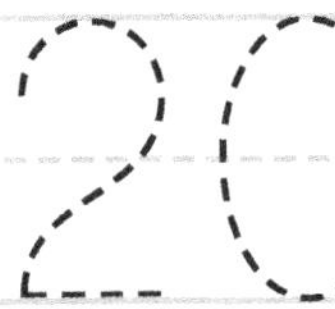

Trace the number word/Traza la palabra numérica.

twenty

veinte
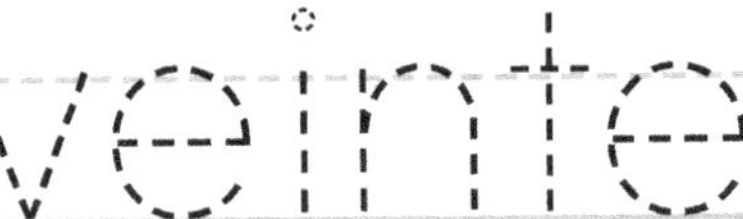
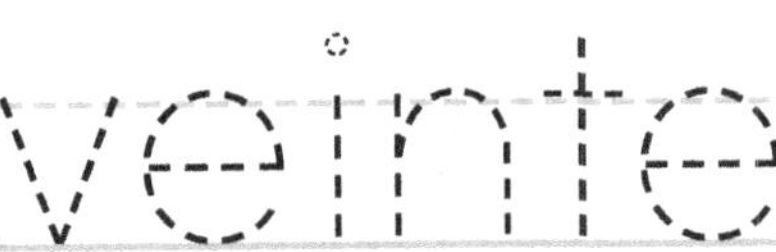

Nombre:.. Fecha:..

Numbers Chart/
Tabla de Números

1	2	3	4	5	6	7	8	9	10
11	12	13	14	15	16	17	18	19	20
21	22	23	24	25	26	27	28	29	30
31	32	33	34	35	36	37	38	39	40
41	42	43	44	45	46	47	48	49	50
51	52	53	54	55	56	57	58	59	60
61	62	63	64	65	66	67	68	69	70
71	72	73	74	75	76	77	78	79	80
81	82	83	84	85	86	87	88	89	90
91	92	93	94	95	96	97	98	99	100

Nombre:.. Fecha:...

Missing Numbers/
Números Perdidos

a) Fill in the missing numbers/Rellenar los números que faltan.

1		3		5		7		9	

b) Fill in the missing numbers/Rellenar los números que faltan.

	12		14	15		17	18		20

c) Fill in the missing numbers/Rellenar los números que faltan.

21			24	25		27		29	

d) Fill in the missing numbers/Rellenar los números que faltan.

31		33		35	36		38		40

e) Fill in the missing numbers/Rellenar los números que faltan.

		43		45		47	48	49	

Nombre:.. Fecha:..

Missing Numbers/
Números Perdidos

a) Fill in the missing numbers/Rellenar los números que faltan.

51			54	55	56			59	

b) Fill in the missing numbers/Rellenar los números que faltan.

	62	63		65	66		68	69	

c) Fill in the missing numbers/Rellenar los números que faltan.

71			74	75			78	79	

d) Fill in the missing numbers/Rellenar los números que faltan.

		83	84		86		88	89	

e) Fill in the missing numbers/Rellenar los números que faltan.

91		93		95	96		98		

Nombre:.. Fecha:..

How Many/
¿Cuántos?

Count how many objects are in each box. Circle correct number/
Cuente cuántos objetos hay en cada caja. Encierra en un círculo el número correcto.

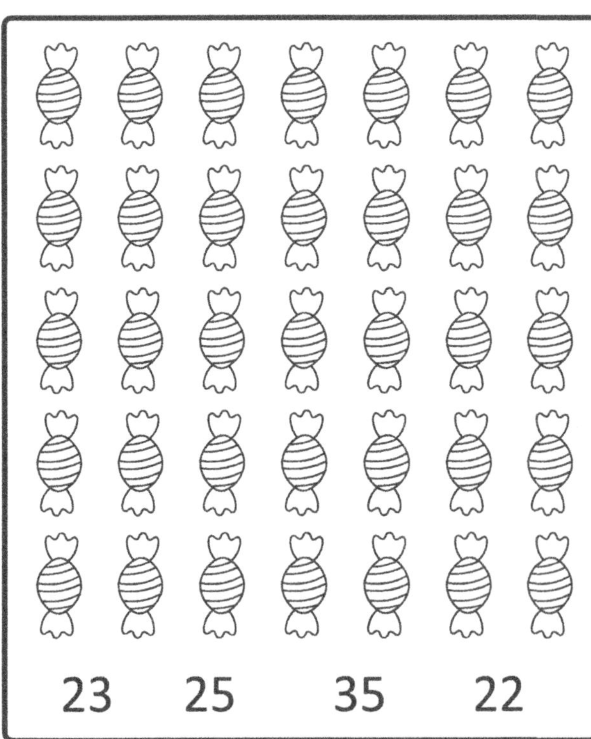

Nombre:.. Fecha:..

How Many/
¿Cuántos?

Count how many pencils are in each box. Then write the correct number/
Cuénta cuántos lápices hay en cada caja. Luego escribe el número correcto.

a) I see .... pencils/Veo..................lápices.

b) I see .... pencils/Veo..................lápices.

c) I see .... pencils/Veo..................lápices.

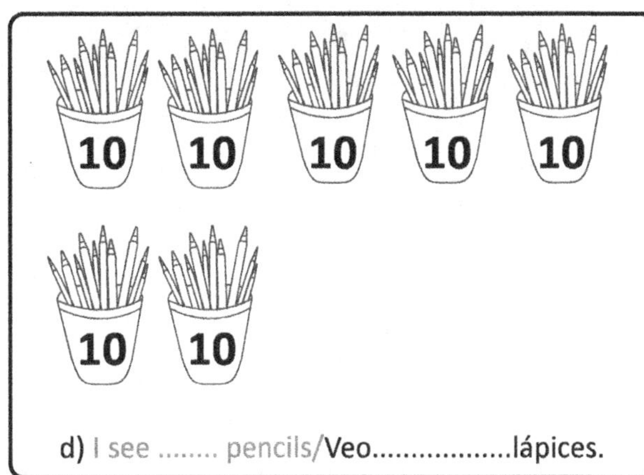

d) I see .... pencils/Veo..................lápices.

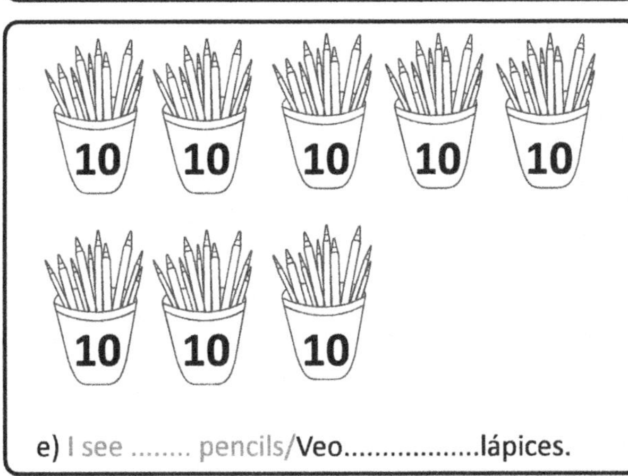

e) I see .... pencils/Veo..................lápices.

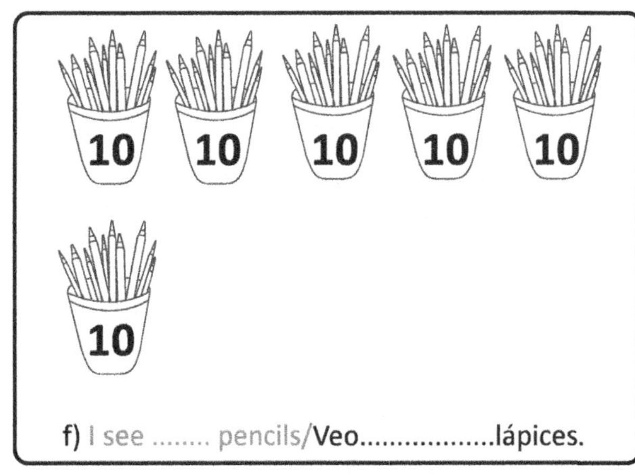

f) I see .... pencils/Veo..................lápices.

g) I see .... pencils/Veo..................lápices.

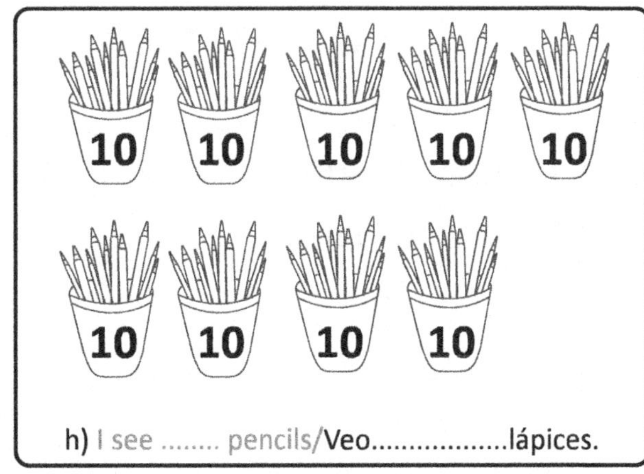

h) I see .... pencils/Veo..................lápices.

Nombre:.. Fecha:..

Color by Number/
Colorear por Numero

Color the picture using the number key/
Colorea el dibujo usando la tecla numérica.

1. Light Brown
1. Marrón Claro

2. Pink
2. Rosa

3. Brown
3. Marrón

Nombre:.. Fecha:..

Color by Number/
Colorear por Numero

Color the picture using the number key/
Colorea el dibujo usando la tecla numérica.

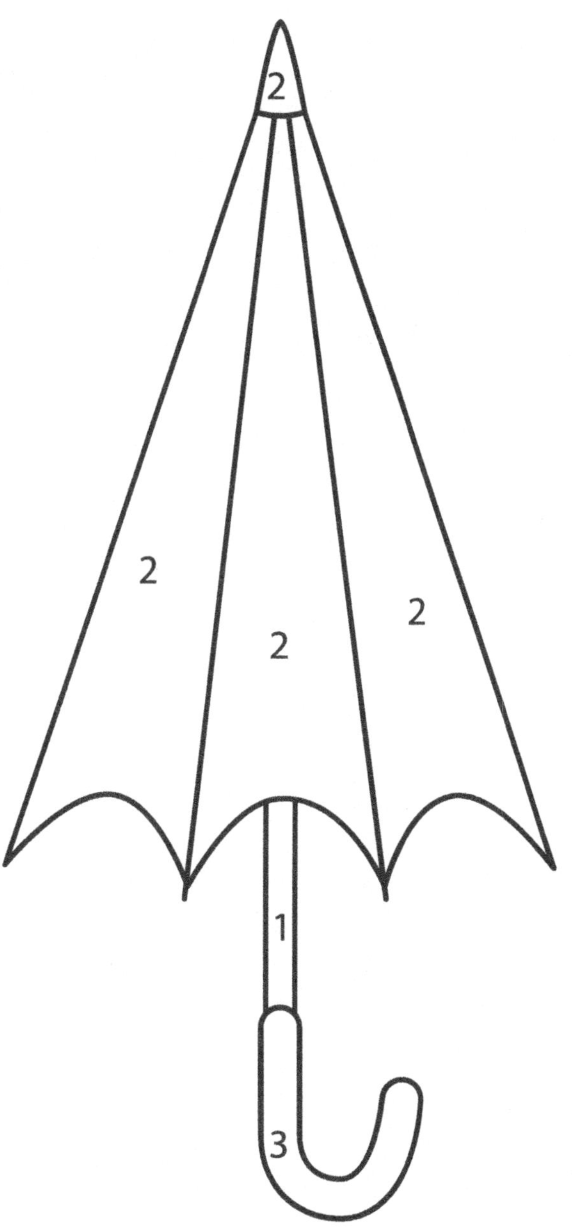

1. Yellow
1. Amarillo

2. Green
2. Verde

3. Brown
3. Marrón

Nombre:.. Fecha:..

Color by Number/
Colorear por Numero

Color the picture using the number key/
Colorea el dibujo usando la tecla numérica.

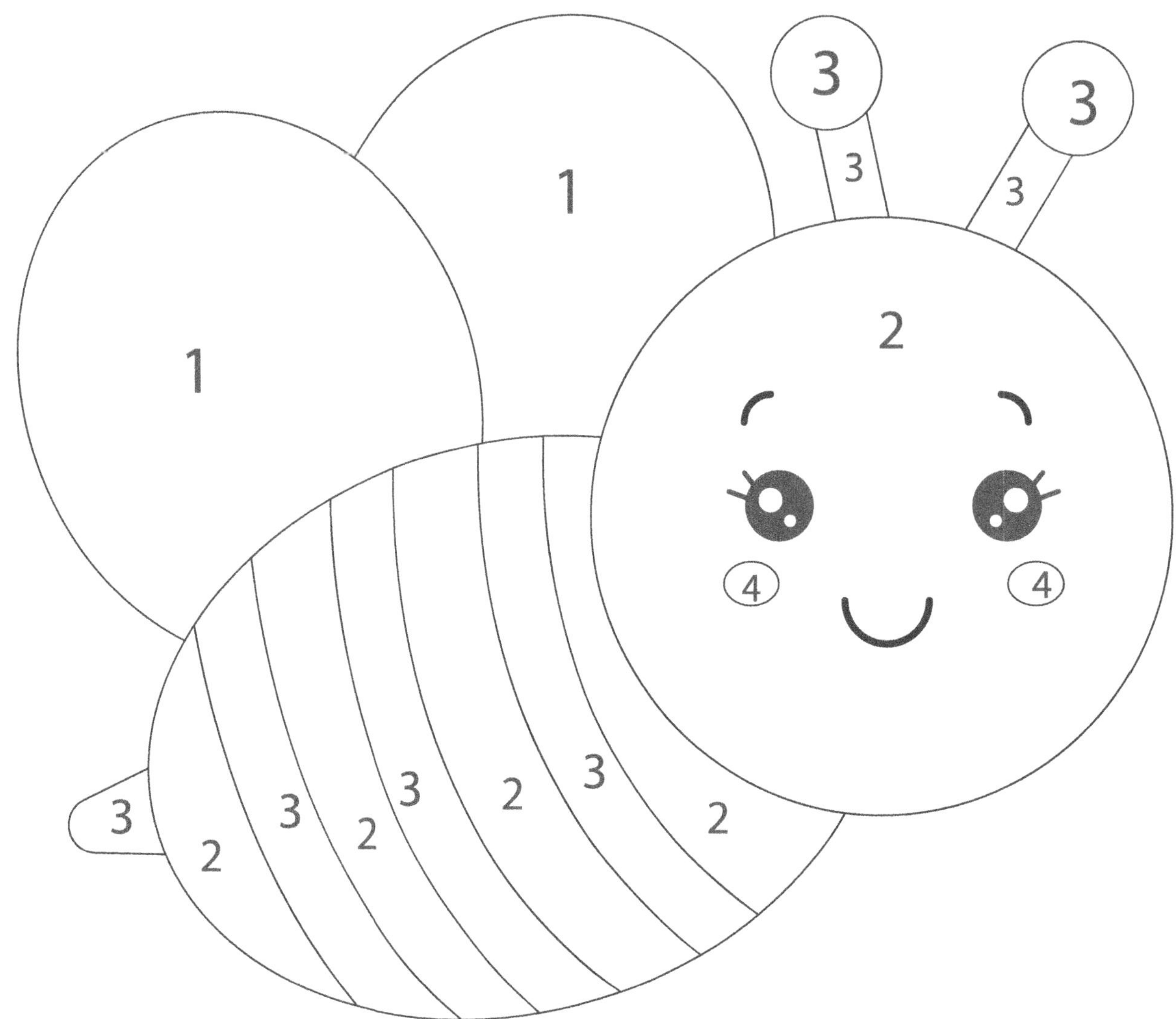

1. Blue
1. Azul

2. Yellow
2. Amarillo

3. Black
3. Negro

4. Pink
4. Rosa

Nombre:.. Fecha:..

Color by Number/
Colorear por Numero

Color the picture using the number key/
Colorea el dibujo usando la tecla numérica.

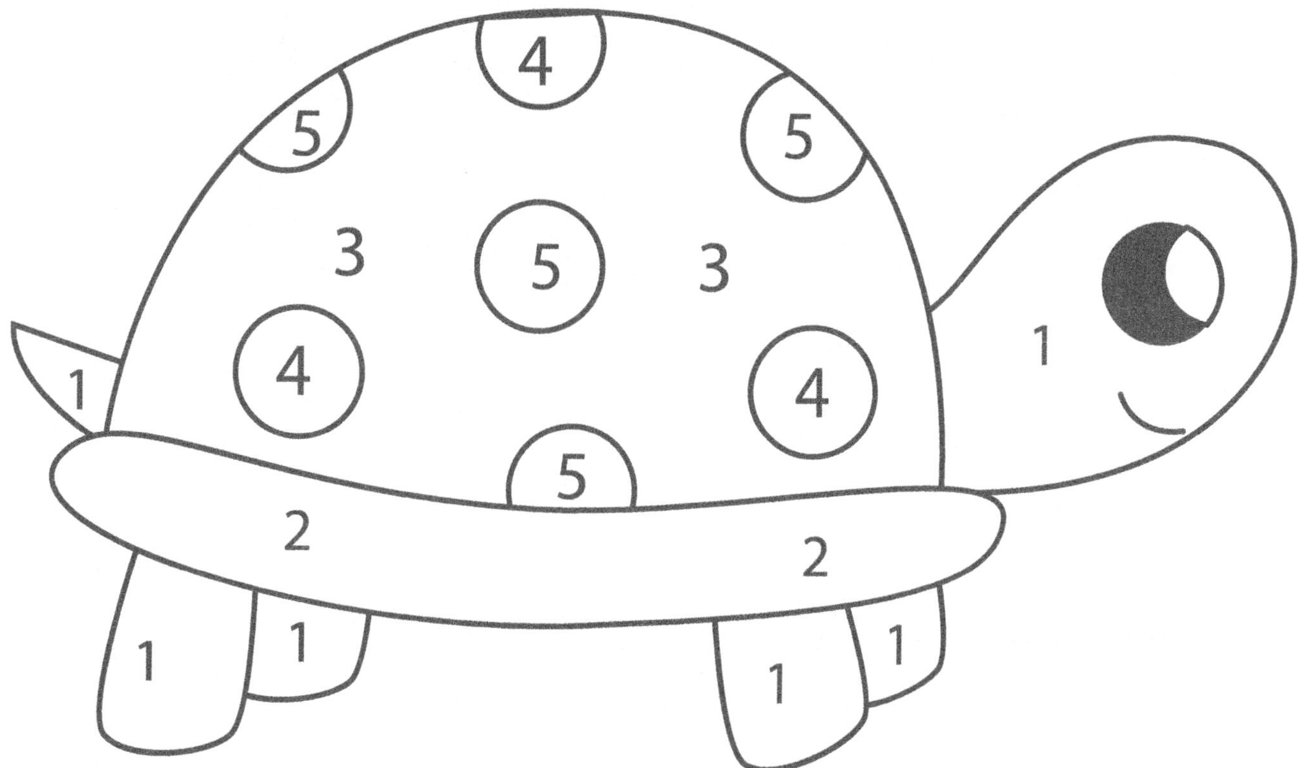

1. Green
1. Verde

2. Brown
2. Marrón

3. Orange
3. Naranja

4. Yellow
4. Amarillo

5. Pink
5. Rosa

Nombre:.. Fecha:..

Color by Number/

Colorear por Numero

Color the picture using the number key/
Colorea el dibujo usando la tecla numérica.

1. Black
1. Negro

2. Yellow
2. Amarillo

3. Orange
3. Naranja

4. Green
4. Verde

5. Brown
5. Marrón

Nombre:... Fecha:...

Dot to Dot/
Punto por Punto

Connect the dots, color the picture and then name what you see/
Conecta los puntos, colorea el dibujo y luego nombra lo que ves.

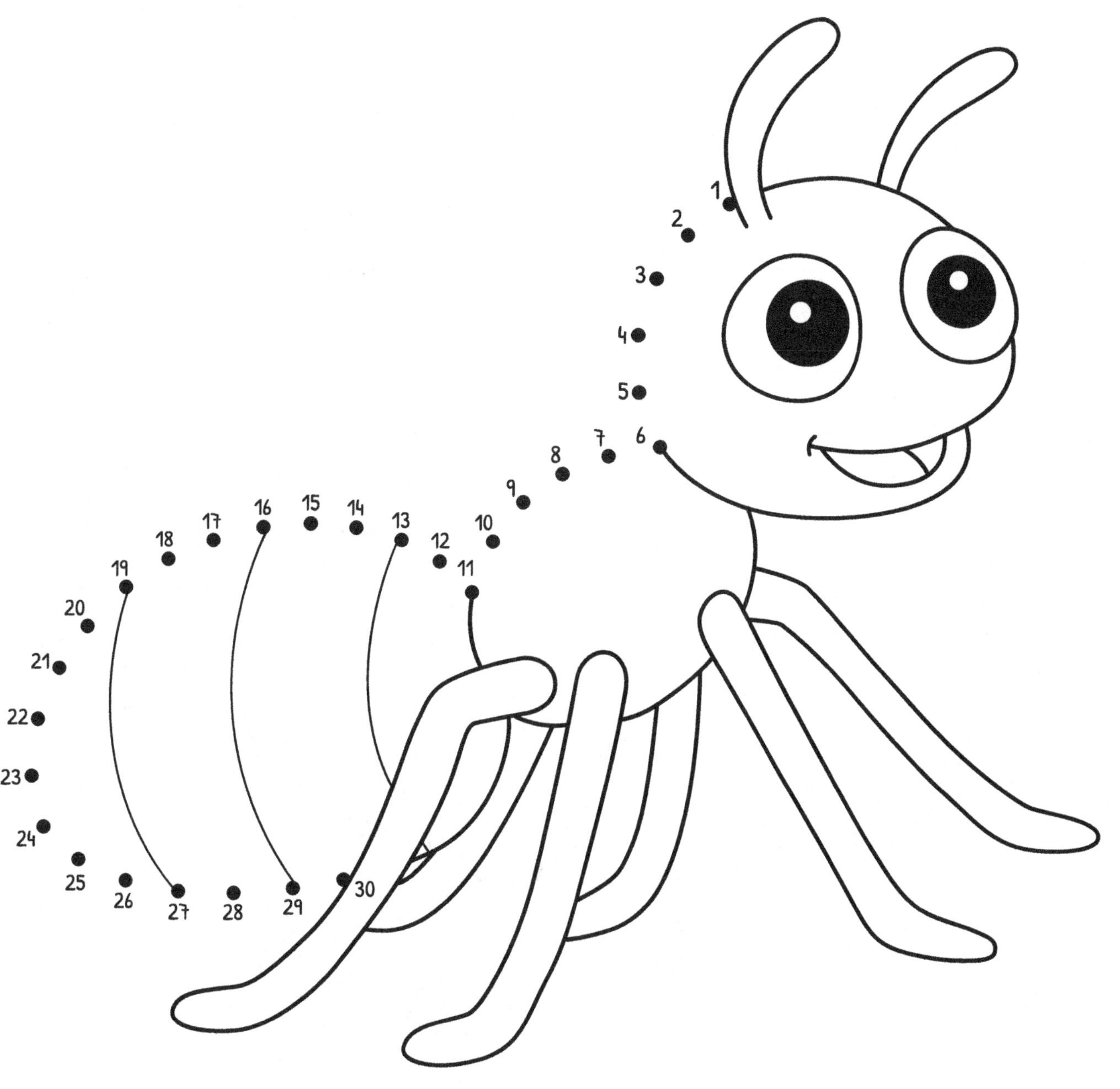

Nombre:.. Fecha:..

Dot to Dot/
Punto por Punto

Connect the dots, color the picture and then name what you see/
Conecta los puntos, colorea el dibujo y luego nombra lo que ves.

Nombre:.. Fecha:..

Dot to Dot/
Punto por Punto

Connect the dots, color the picture and then name what you see/
Conecta los puntos, colorea el dibujo y luego nombra lo que ves.

Nombre:... Fecha:...

Dot to Dot/
Punto por Punto

Connect the dots, color the picture and then name what you see/
Conecta los puntos, colorea el dibujo y luego nombra lo que ves.

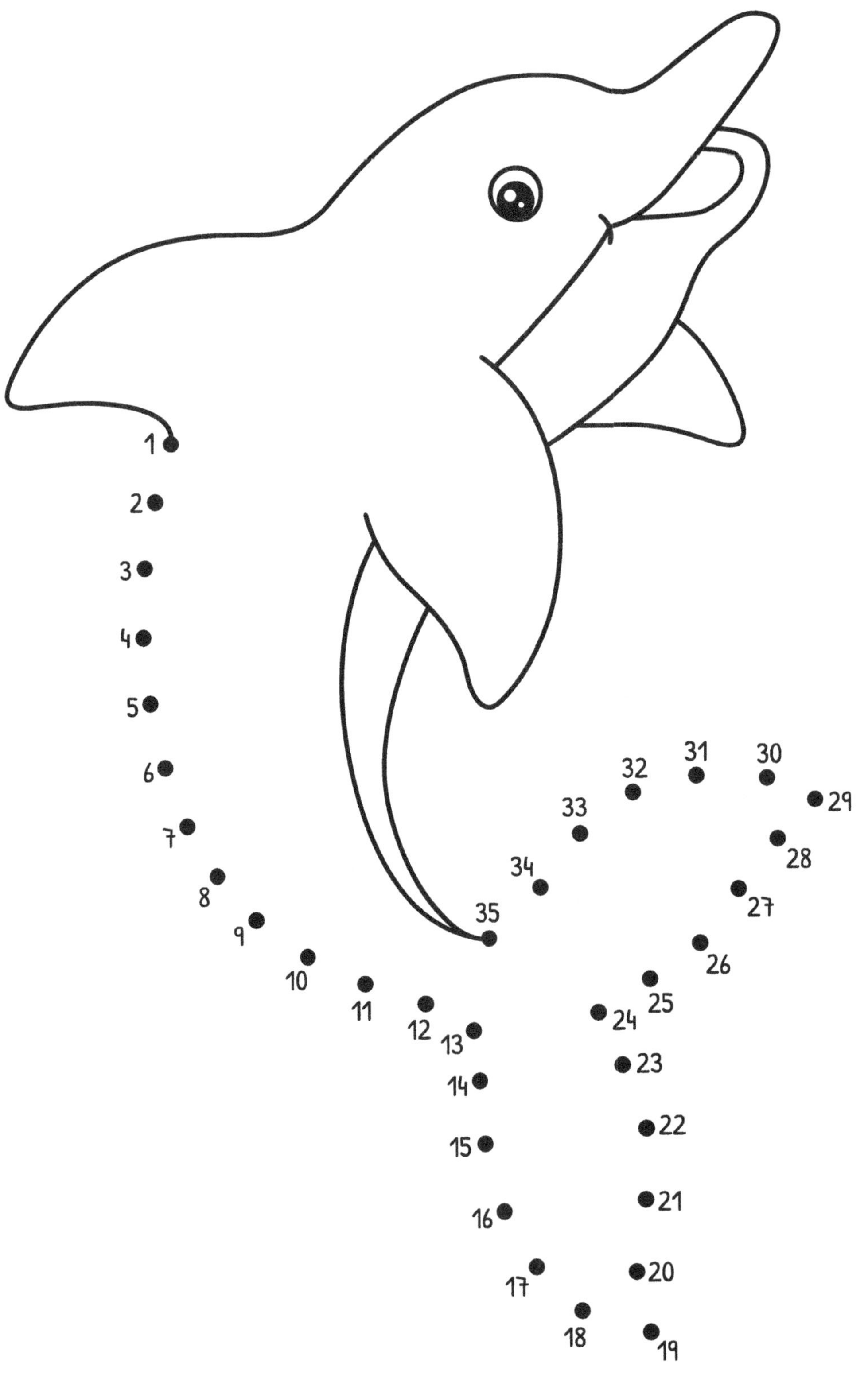

Nombre:.. Fecha:..

Dot to Dot/
Punto por Punto

Connect the dots, color the picture and then name what you see/
Conecta los puntos, colorea el dibujo y luego nombra lo que ves.

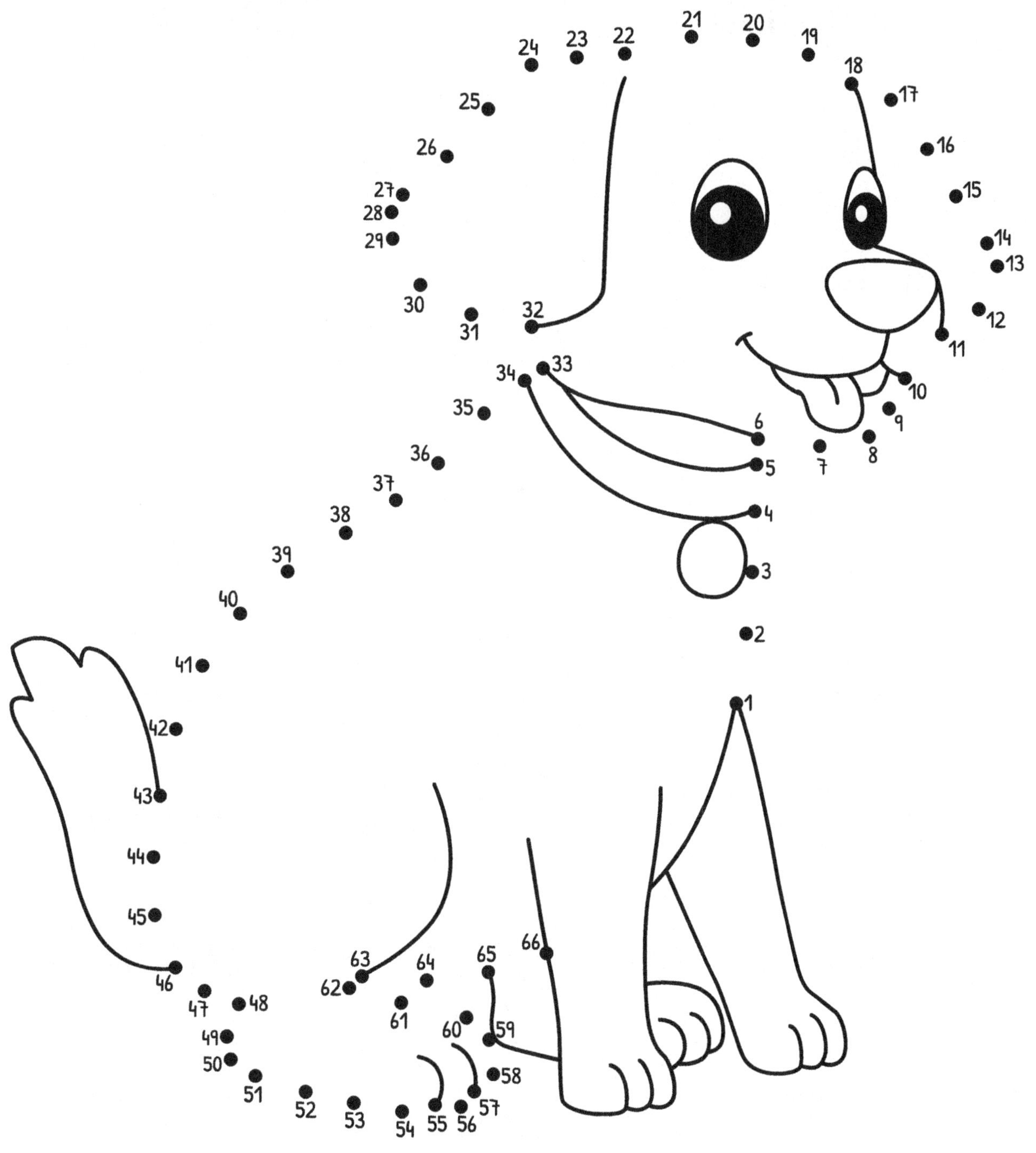

Nombre:..   Fecha:..

Shapes and Colors/
Formas y Colores

Trace, color and say the shape out loud/
Traza, colorea y di la forma en voz alta.

English		Spanish
Square		Cuadrado
Rectangle		Rectángulo
Triangle		Triángulo
Circle		Círculo
Oval		Óvalo
Diamond		Diamante
Star		Estrella
Heart		Corazón
Pentagon		Pentágono

Nombre:..   Fecha:..

Shapes and Colors/
Formas y Colores

Color the shapes and then draw lines to match each image's shadow/
Colorea las formas y luego dibuja líneas que coincidan con la sombra de cada imagen.

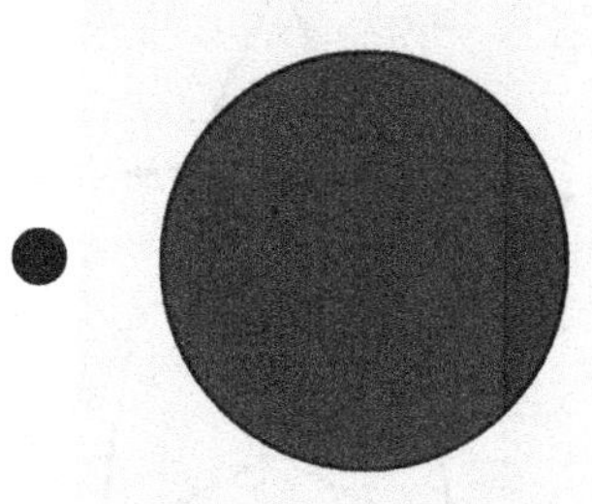

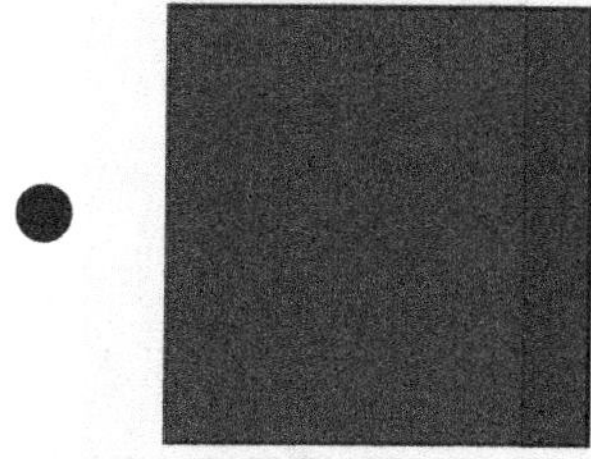

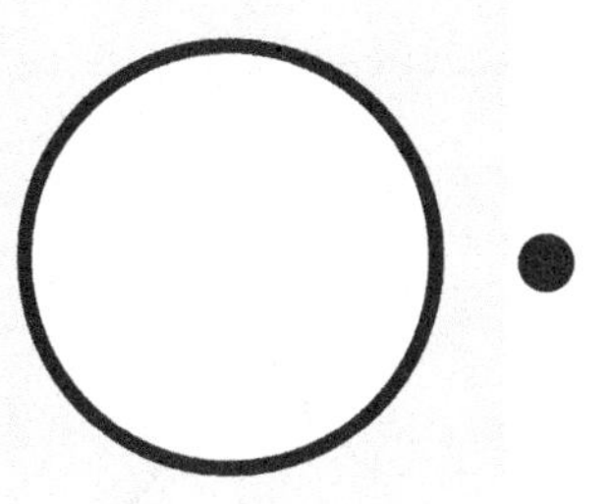
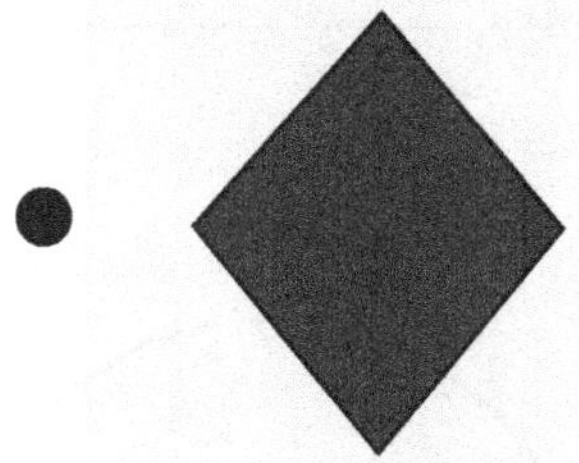

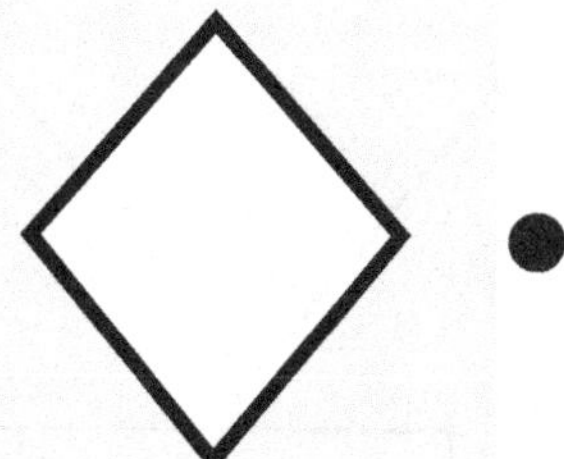

Nombre:.. Fecha:..

Shapes and Colors/
Formas y Colores

Look at each shape and write down its name. Then pick your favorite color/
Mira cada forma y escribe su nombre. Luego elige tu color favorito.

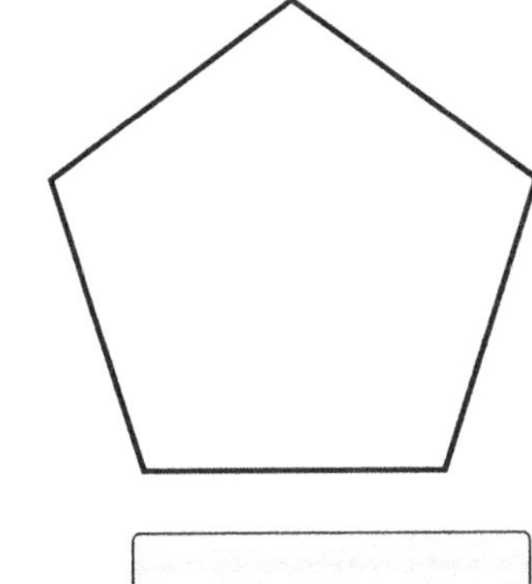

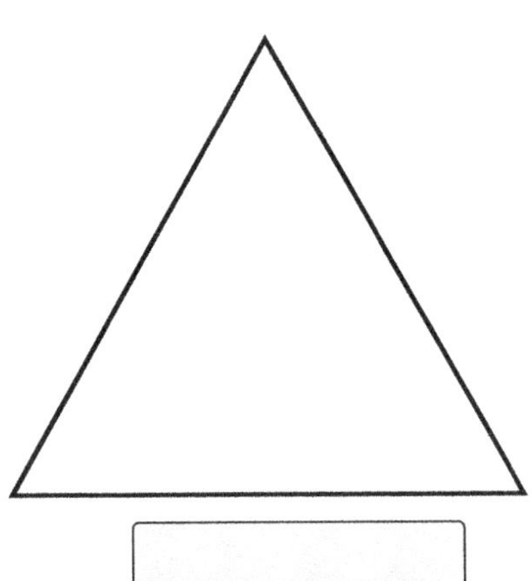

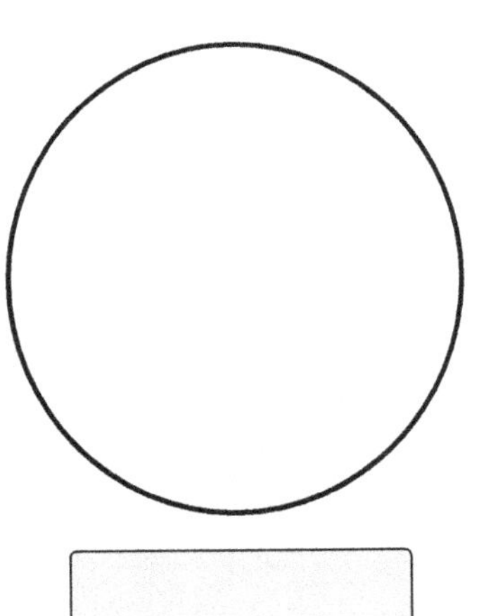

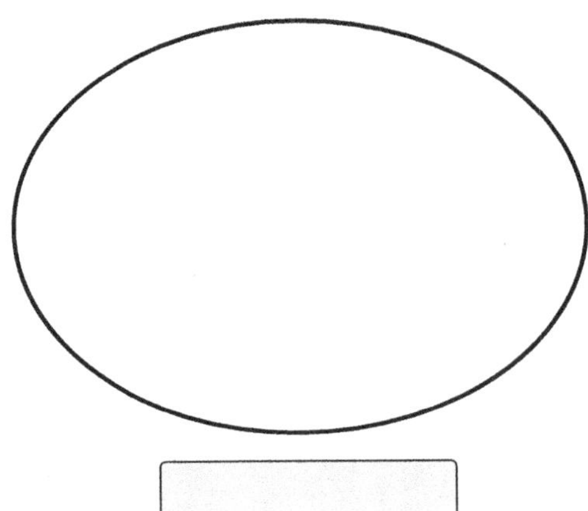

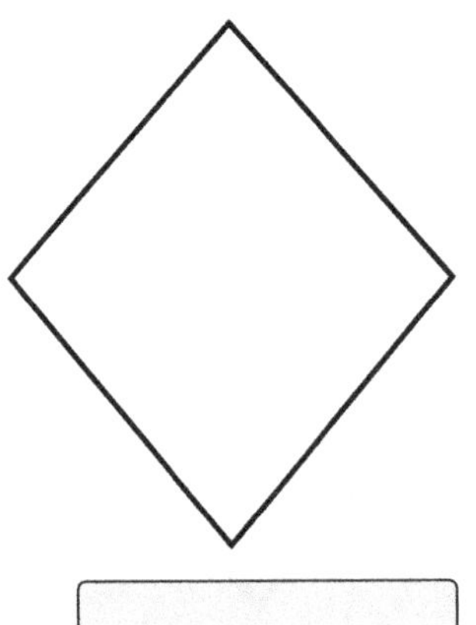

Nombre:.. Fecha:..

Shapes and Colors/
Formas y Colores

Can you count how many shapes there are? Then pick your favorite color/
¿Puedes contar cuántas formas hay? Luego elige tu color favorito.

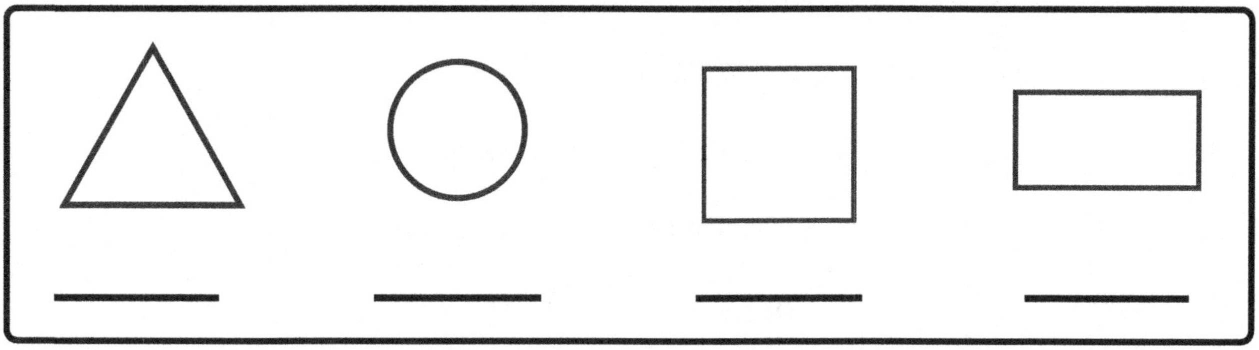

Nombre:.. Fecha:..

Shapes and Colors/
Formas y Colores

1. Color the ◯ red/Colorea el ◯ rojo.
2. Color the □ green/Colorea el □ verde.
3. Color the △ blue/Colorea el △ azul.
4. Color the ☆ yellow/Colorea el ☆ amarillo.
5 Color the ♡ pink/Colorea el ♡ rosa.

Nombre:.. Fecha:..

Word Scramble/
Sopa de Letras

Unscramble the letters to spell the words correctl/
Descifra las letras para escribir las palabras correctamente.

English	Spanish	
1) car	hcoce	____________
2) bus	asbútuo	____________
3) train	etnr	____________
4) bicycle	tbaiieclc	____________
5) boat	raocb	____________
6) plane	iaónv	____________
7) helicopter	itceoólehrp	____________
8) motorcycle	coomticleat	____________
9) truck	anmció	____________
10) ship	oacrb	____________
11) submarine	orasuibmn	____________
12) balloon	loogb	____________
13) skateboard	tpeanita	____________
14) jet	croorh	____________
15) tram	arníatv	____________

Nombre:.. Fecha:..

Word Scramble/
Sopa de Letras

Unscramble the letters to spell the words correctl/
Descifra las letras para escribir las palabras correctamente.

English	Spanish	
1) cow	vaac	________________
2) pig	rocde	________________
3) chicken	lloop	________________
4) sheep	evjao	________________
5) goat	barac	________________
6) horse	ablalco	________________
7) duck	tpoa	________________
8) turkey	vaop	________________
9) donkey	rurob	________________
10) rabbit	coejon	________________
11) goose	ongas	________________
12) dog	rpero	________________
13) cat	toag	________________
14) goat	abcra	________________
15) llama	llaam	________________

Nombre:.. Fecha:..

Word Scramble/
Sopa de Letras

Unscramble the letters to spell the words correctl/
Descifra las letras para escribir las palabras correctamente.

English	Spanish	
1) lion	eónl	________________
2) tiger	iegrt	________________
3) elephant	enteafle	________________
4) giraffe	ijafar	________________
5) monkey	nmoo	________________
6) gorilla	grlaio	________________
7) zebra	cbrae	________________
8) hippo	hmooiptapó	________________
9) crocodile	oiooclrdc	________________
10) jaguar	rjuaag	________________
11) snake	entpesrie	________________
12) panther	atarnpe	________________
13) parrot	loro	________________
14) chimpanzee	acmhnépic	________________
15) rhinoceros	nooneecritr	________________

Nombre:.. Fecha:..

Word Scramble/
Sopa de Letras

Unscramble the letters to spell the words correctl/
Descifra las letras para escribir las palabras correctamente.

English	Spanish	
1) apple	znaanma	____________
2) banana	nolpaát	____________
3) orange	rnnajaa	____________
4) strawberry	esfar	____________
5) pineapple	pañi	____________
6) mango	agmno	____________
7) grape	avu	____________
8) watermelon	ansdía	____________
9) peach	ócmeolnot	____________
10) pear	prea	____________
11) cherry	erczea	____________
12) lemon	óilnm	____________
13) kiwi	wkii	____________
14) blueberry	nroaáand	____________
15) raspberry	ameasubfr	____________

Nombre:.. Fecha:..

Word Scramble/
Sopa de Letras

Unscramble the letters to spell the words correctl/
Descifra las letras para escribir las palabras correctamente.

English	Spanish	
1) backpack	omilcah	____________
2) notebook	rcenuoad	____________
3) pencil	lázip	____________
4) pen	aumlp	____________
5) eraser	ooarrbdr	____________
6) ruler	realg	____________
7) book	libor	____________
8) calculator	oaarulcldca	____________
9) marker	mcodrara	____________
10) glue	tegeoapmn	____________
11) scissors	stairej	____________
12) folder	eatrapc	____________
13) highlighter	mdcoaarr	____________
14) pencil case	euehsct	____________
15) sharpener	sspncaauta	____________

Nombre:.. Fecha:..

Word Search/
Búsqueda de Palabras

Find and circle the words hidden in the puzzle. The words have been placed horizontally, vertically, or backward./
Encuentra y rodea con un círculo las palabras escondidas en el rompecabezas.Las palabras se han colocado horizontal, vertical o al revés.

H	D	A	L	L	O	B	E	C	C	Ó	Ó	Ó	G
Z	O	B	E	B	A	T	A	T	A	P	R	Z	H
S	Ó	Ó	J	T	U	N	W	X	D	Q	P	Q	R
U	T	U	Y	O	N	I	P	E	P	O	A	E	O
Y	N	T	I	P	C	I	W	X	O	J	K	O	L
S	Y	M	U	A	P	Ó	U	V	E	A	Y	E	F
Q	A	I	R	O	H	A	N	A	Z	L	P	B	I
H	A	R	P	V	E	O	Ó	B	P	E	I	R	L
H	Z	B	E	P	X	S	P	Y	L	C	M	Ó	O
E	E	T	A	M	O	T	P	Ó	W	H	I	C	C
Y	Q	B	O	J	B	V	L	N	B	U	E	O	Ó
N	Y	E	Z	E	J	V	B	B	K	G	N	L	O
Z	D	T	E	N	I	R	D	L	W	A	T	I	U
D	X	U	M	P	W	R	K	Q	F	C	O	U	W

Word List/Lista de Palabras

English	Spanish
CARROT	ZANAHORIA
POTATO	PATATA
TOMATO	TOMATE
CUCUMBER	PEPINO
LETTUCE	LECHUGA
ONION	CEBOLLA
GARLIC	AJO
BELL PEPPER	PIMIENTO
BROCCOLI	BRÓCOLI
CAULIFLOWER	COLIFLOR

Nombre:.. Fecha:..

Word Search/
Búsqueda de Palabras

Find and circle the words hidden in the puzzle. The words have been placed horizontally, vertically, or backward./
Encuentra y rodea con un círculo las palabras escondidas en el rompecabezas.Las palabras se han colocado horizontal, vertical o al revés.

Z	M	T	P	T	W	Ñ	D	E	E	Z	I	D	L
I	Ñ	P	L	Ñ	R	T	R	E	N	R	I	T	G
P	L	A	S	T	I	L	I	N	A	Y	C	E	E
R	O	M	P	E	C	A	B	E	Z	A	S	H	Z
N	M	C	D	Q	S	B	F	O	F	G	E	C	O
M	M	Z	T	G	D	H	A	S	W	Y	A	O	S
T	A	A	C	E	Ñ	U	M	Z	B	M	O	C	O
P	N	W	G	Z	C	A	F	P	I	N	S	J	T
Q	I	R	I	C	U	X	H	R	E	I	E	H	T
S	M	P	E	L	O	T	A	E	A	Q	U	T	U
S	A	O	D	L	V	J	D	W	D	Z	Q	Z	I
U	L	V	V	Y	L	U	G	B	H	H	O	D	C
Ñ	Ñ	L	I	B	R	O	Ñ	G	Z	O	L	B	E
B	R	Z	H	S	Ñ	Ñ	J	T	U	N	B	W	X

Word List/Lista de Palabras

English	Spanish
DOLL	MUÑECA
BEAR	OSO
BALL	PELOTA
CAR	COCHE
BLOCKS	BLOQUES
PUZZLE	ROMPECABEZAS
ANIMAL	ANIMAL
TRAIN	TREN
BOOK	LIBRO
DOUGH	PLASTILINA

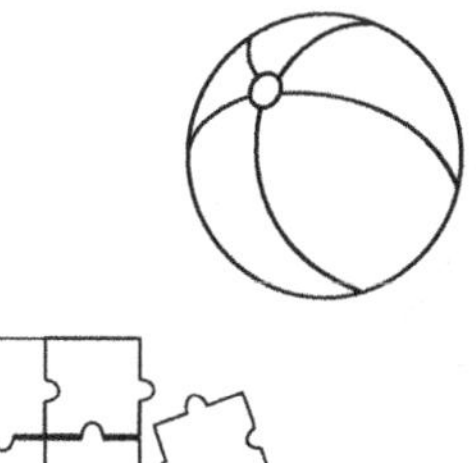

Nombre:... Fecha:...

Word Search/
Búsqueda de Palabras

Find and circle the words hidden in the puzzle. The words have been placed horizontally, vertically, or backward./
Encuentra y rodea con un círculo las palabras escondidas en el rompecabezas.Las palabras se han colocado horizontal, vertical o al revés.

F	Á	Á	L	V	X	G	H	D	L	Z	M	T	P
O	T	W	Á	D	E	E	Z	I	D	L	I	Á	P
J	L	Á	R	R	I	T	G	Y	C	E	Z	N	M
E	C	A	R	B	M	O	F	L	A	D	Q	Á	S
P	B	F	O	F	G	E	M	M	Z	T	G	F	M
S	D	A	H	A	S	W	Y	A	T	Z	B	O	E
E	J	L	M	A	M	A	C	O	C	P	W	S	S
G	O	L	Z	C	A	F	P	I	O	N	A	J	A
T	L	I	Q	R	I	C	U	X	R	H	R	R	E
I	E	S	H	T	S	E	A	Q	T	T	A	U	S
O	R	D	L	V	J	D	W	D	I	Z	P	Z	I
U	V	E	S	T	A	N	T	E	N	V	M	Y	L
U	G	B	H	H	D	C	Á	Á	A	Á	Á	G	Z
O	B	E	B	R	Z	H	S	Á	Á	J	L	T	U

Word List/Lista de Palabras

English	Spanish
BED	CAMA
TABLE	MESA
CHAIR	SILLA
SOFA	SOFÁ
LAMP	LÁMPARA
RUG	ALFOMBRA
CURTAIN	CORTINA
MIRROR	ESPEJO
CLOCK	RELOJ
SHELF	ESTANTE

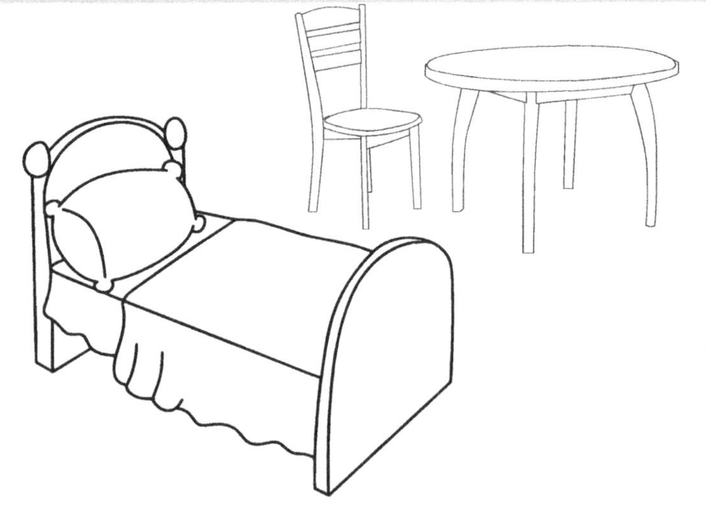

Nombre:.. Fecha:..

Word Search/
Búsqueda de Palabras

Find and circle the words hidden in the puzzle. The words have been placed horizontally, vertically, or backward./
Encuentra y rodea con un círculo las palabras escondidas en el rompecabezas.Las palabras se han colocado horizontal, vertical o al revés.

U	G	B	H	H	D	C	G	Z	O	B	E	B	R
Z	H	A	G	L	A	S	J	T	U	N	W	X	D
Q	P	Q	U	T	U	Y	A	E	Y	N	T	I	P
C	I	W	X	A	I	B	B	A	S	O	J	A	K
O	S	Y	M	U	A	P	U	V	E	Y	E	D	A
Q	H	A	R	P	V	E	O	B	P	H	Z	N	C
B	E	O	N	A	E	C	O	P	S	X	A	O	Q
S	A	I	L	G	I	H	C	N	O	C	I	N	U
P	Y	L	E	P	W	Y	Q	B	L	O	G	I	A
J	B	P	E	S	C	E	V	L	E	N	G	F	B
N	Y	E	Z	E	J	V	B	B	K	O	A	L	Z
D	T	E	N	I	R	D	L	W	L	U	I	E	D
X	U	M	P	W	R	K	Q	F	F	C	P	D	U
W	P	I	J	U	W	K	N	W	T	L	S	U	C

Word List/Lista de Palabras

English	Spanish
OCEAN	OCÉANO
WATER	AGUA
FISH	PESCADO
WAVE	OLA
BEACH	PLAYA
SAND	ARENA
SUN	SOL
SHELL	CONCHA
SEAWEED	ALGA
DOLPHIN	DELFÍN

Nombre:... Fecha:...

Word Search/
Búsqueda de Palabras

Find and circle the words hidden in the puzzle. The words have been placed horizontally, vertically, or backward./
Encuentra y rodea con un círculo las palabras escondidas en el rompecabezas.Las palabras se han colocado horizontal, vertical o al revés.

S	J	T	U	N	W	X	D	Q	P	Q	U	T	U
Y	A	E	Y	N	T	I	P	C	I	W	X	O	J
K	O	S	Y	M	U	A	P	U	V	E	Y	E	Q
H	A	O	M	S	I	L	C	I	C	R	P	V	E
O	O	R	T	S	E	N	A	C	A	L	L	A	P
B	P	H	Z	B	E	P	X	S	P	L	Y	L	E
P	W	O	I	C	L	A	C	Y	Q	L	B	N	H
O	O	L	O	V	A	L	L	A	P	A	B	U	O
V	L	N	B	N	Y	E	Z	E	J	B	V	O	C
B	B	T	E	N	N	I	S	K	O	E	A	T	K
Z	D	T	E	N	I	R	D	F	L	S	S	O	E
W	L	U	D	X	U	M	P	L	W	A	R	R	Y
K	Q	F	F	C	U	W	P	O	I	B	O	J	U
W	K	N	W	T	L	U	C	G	X	S	C	G	L

Word List/Lista de Palabras

English	Spanish
SOCCER	FÚTBOL
BASKETBALL	BALONCESTO
TENNIS	TENIS
SWIMMING	NATACIÓN
RUNNING	CORRER
CYCLING	CICLISMO
VOLLEYBALL	VOLEIBOL
GOLF	GOLF
BASEBALL	BÉISBOL
HOCKEY	HOCKEY

Nombre:.. Fecha:..

Maze/
Laberinto

Help the hungry panda to find the delicious bamboo/
Ayuda al panda hambriento a encontrar el delicioso bambú.

Nombre:.. Fecha:..

Maze/
Laberinto

Help the baby giraffe get to the palm tree/
Ayuda a la jirafa bebé a llegar a la palmera.

Nombre:.. Fecha:..

Maze/

Laberinto

Help the Buzzy Bee through the maze to collect sweet nectar from the flowers/

¡Ayuda a Buzzy Bee a través del laberinto para recolectar el dulce néctar de las flores!

Nombre:.. Fecha:..

Maze/

Laberinto

Help the hungry cow find its way to delicious green grass/

¡Ayuda a la vaca hambrienta a encontrar el camino hacia la deliciosa hierba verde!

Nombre:.. Fecha:..

Maze/
Laberinto

Help the hungry dog through the maze to find its tasty bone/
Ayuda al perro hambriento a atravesar el laberinto para encontrar su sabroso hueso.

Nombre:... Fecha:...

Spot the Differences/
Encuentra las diferencias

Compare the two pictures and spot 5 difference/
Compara las dos imágenes y encuentra 5 diferencias.

Nombre:.. Fecha:..

Spot the Differences/
Encuentra las diferencias

Compare the two pictures and spot 5 difference/
Compara las dos imágenes y encuentra 5 diferencias.

Nombre:.. Fecha:..

Spot the Differences/

Encuentra las diferencias

Compare the two pictures and spot 5 difference/

Compara las dos imágenes y encuentra 5 diferencias.

Nombre:.. Fecha:..

Spot the Differences/
Encuentra las diferencias

Compare the two pictures and spot 5 difference/
Compara las dos imágenes y encuentra 5 diferencias.

Nombre:.. Fecha:..

Spot the Differences/
Encuentra las diferencias

Compare the two pictures and spot 5 difference/
Compara las dos imágenes y encuentra 5 diferencias.

Nombre:.. Fecha:..

I Spy/
Veo, Veo

Count each object and write the correct number in the box/
Cuente cada objeto y escriba el número correcto en el cuadro.

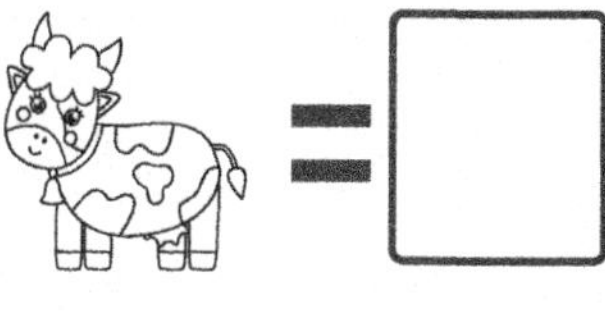

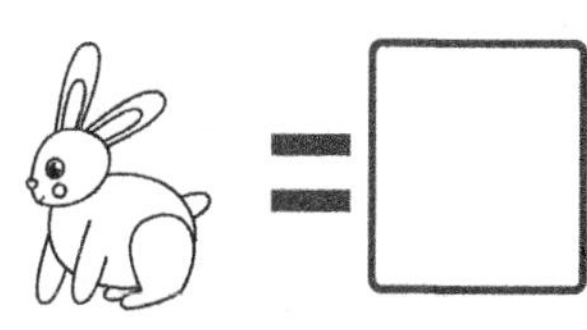

Nombre:.. Fecha:..

I Spy/
Veo, Veo

Count each object and write the correct number in the box/
Cuente cada objeto y escriba el número correcto en el cuadro.

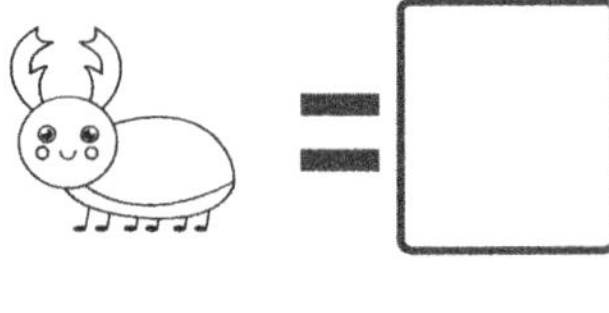

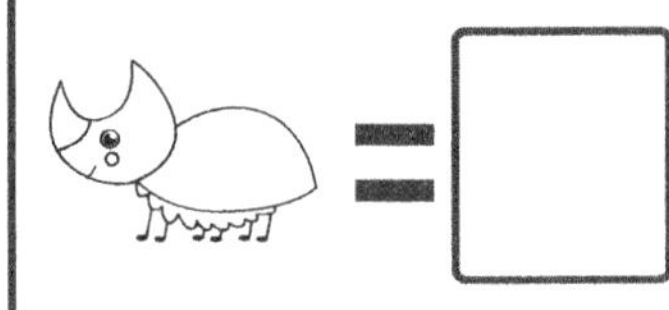

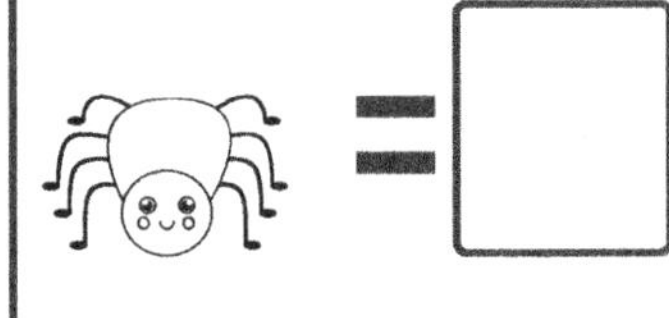

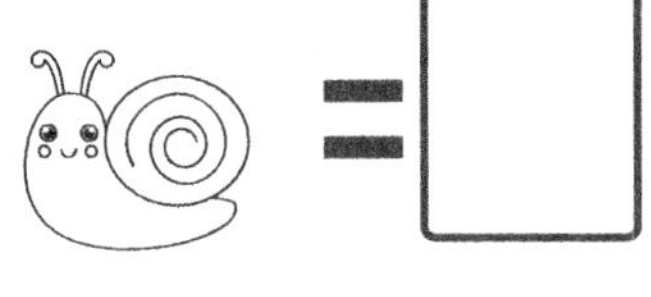

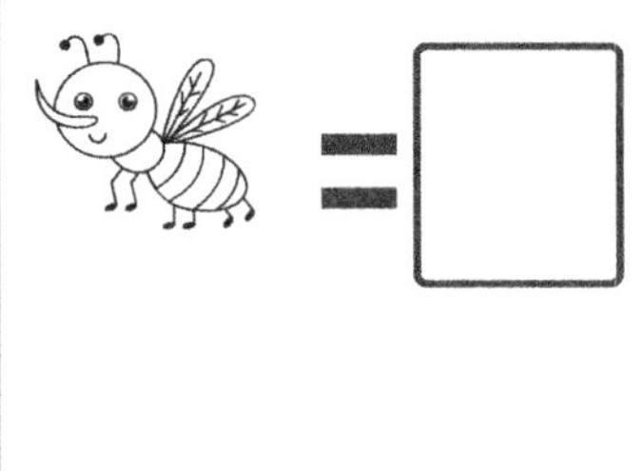

Nombre:... Fecha:...

I Spy/
Veo, Veo

Count each object and write the correct number in the box/
Cuente cada objeto y escriba el número correcto en el cuadro.

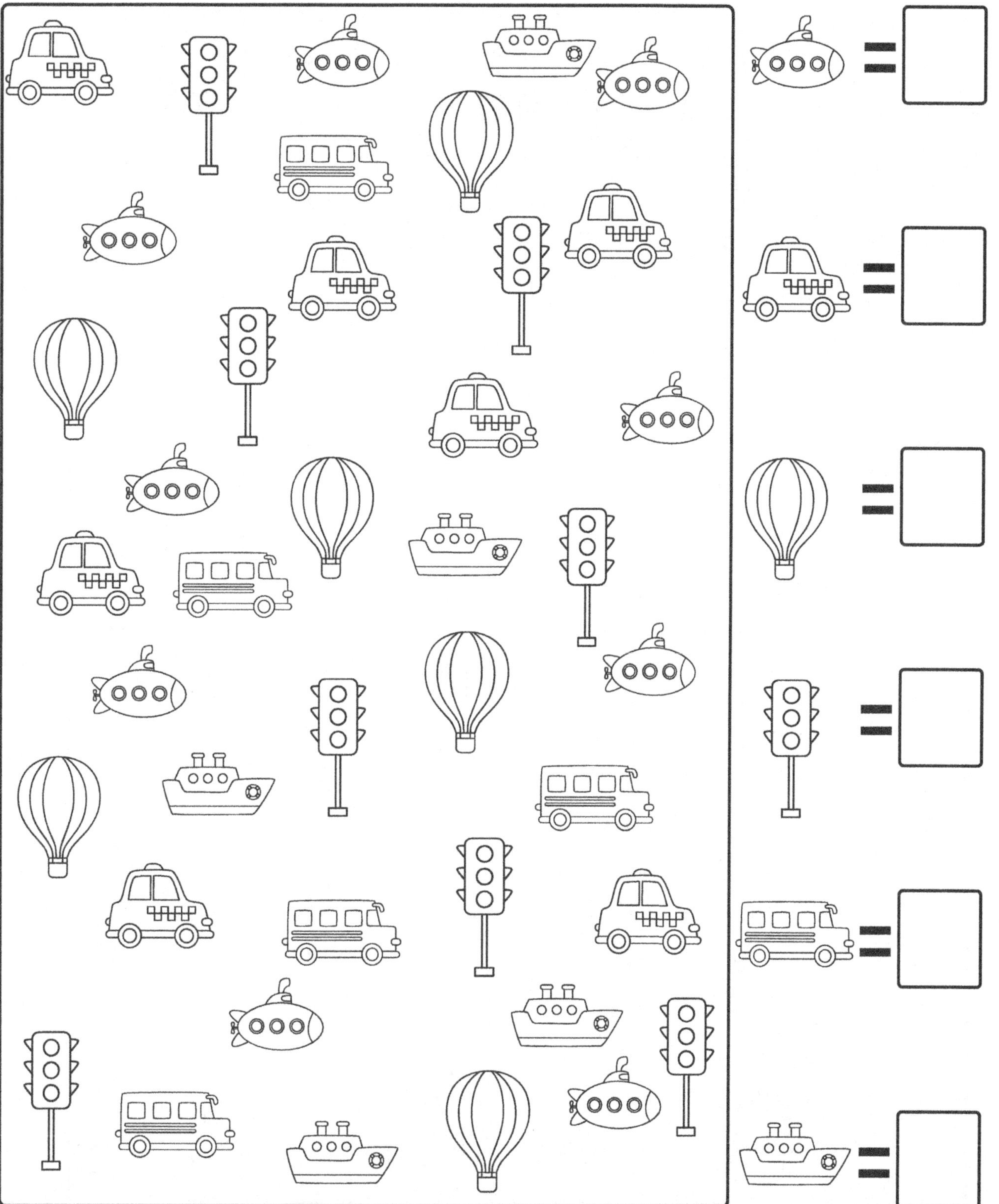

Nombre:.. Fecha:..

I Spy/
Veo, Veo

Count each object and write the correct number in the box/
Cuente cada objeto y escriba el número correcto en el cuadro.

Nombre:.. Fecha:..

I Spy/
Veo, Veo

Count each object and write the correct number in the box/
Cuente cada objeto y escriba el número correcto en el cuadro.

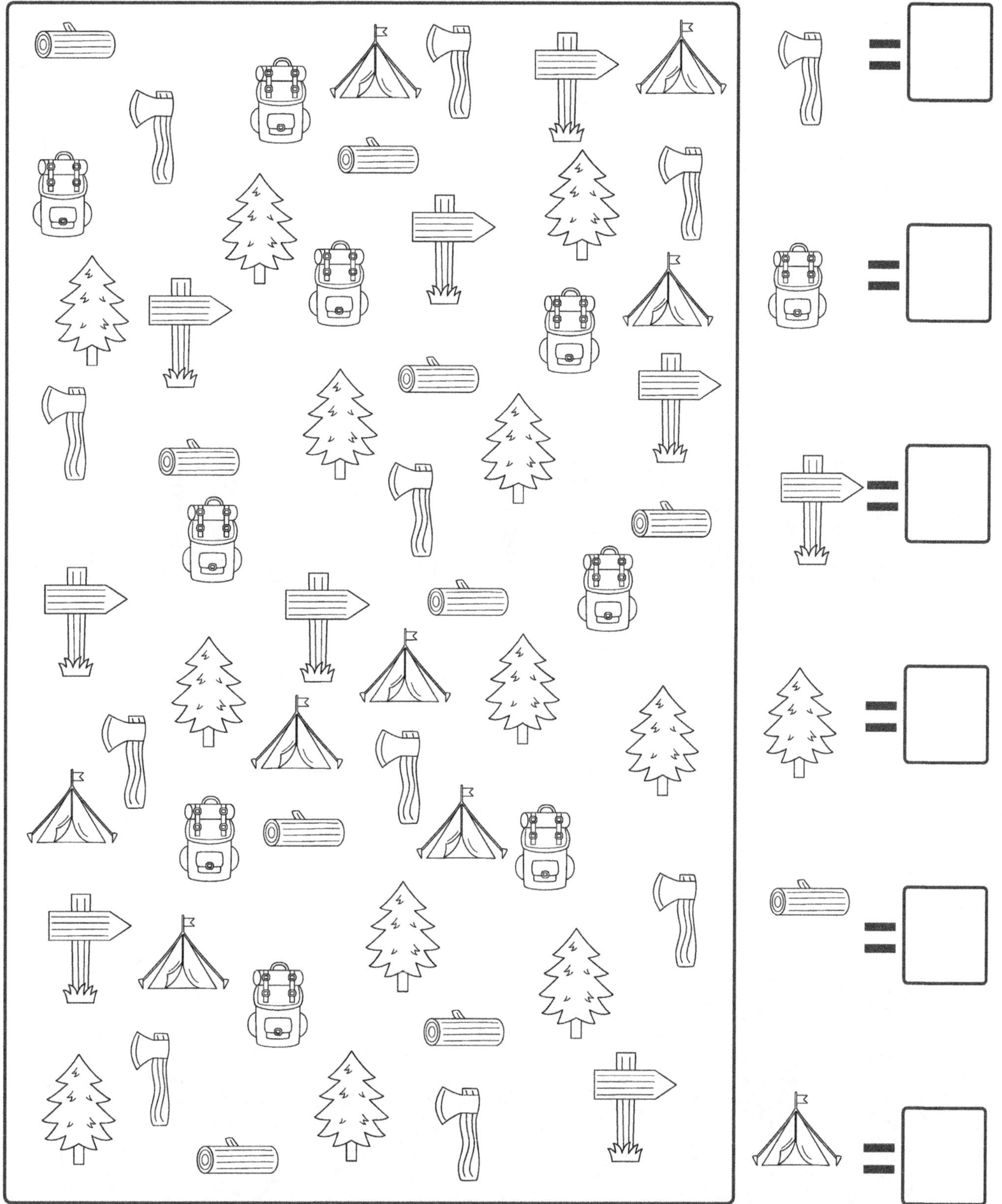

SOLUTION

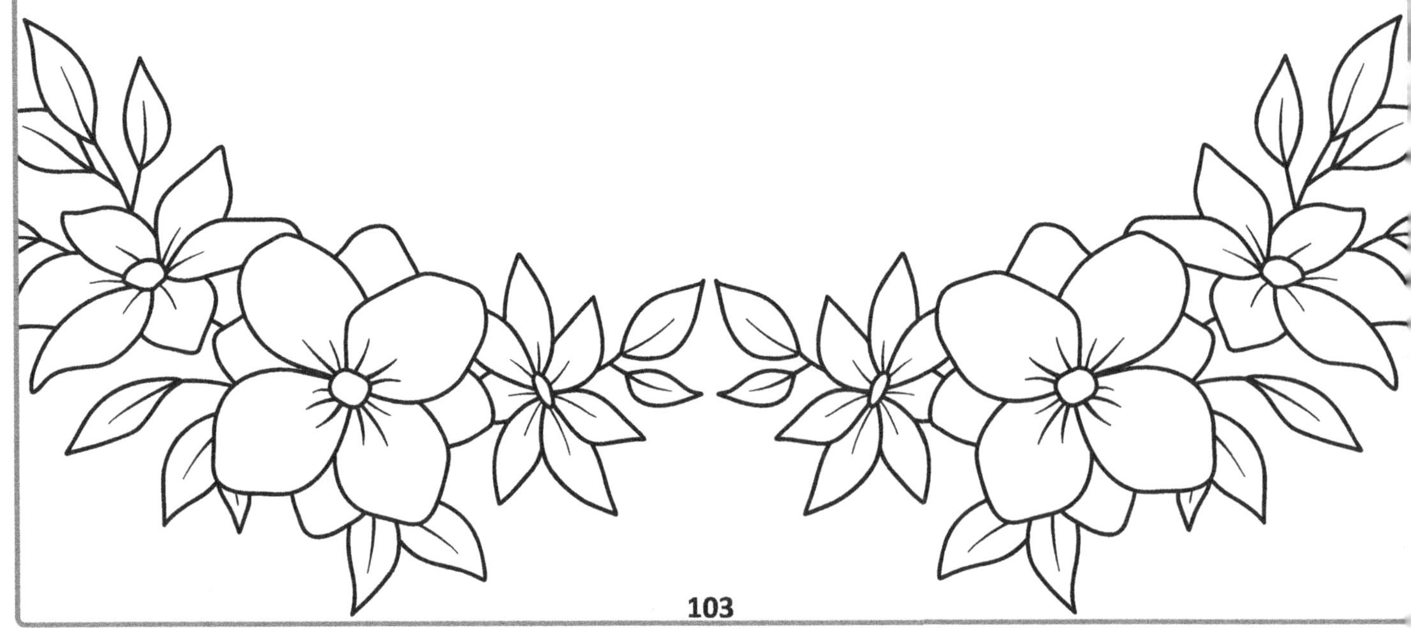

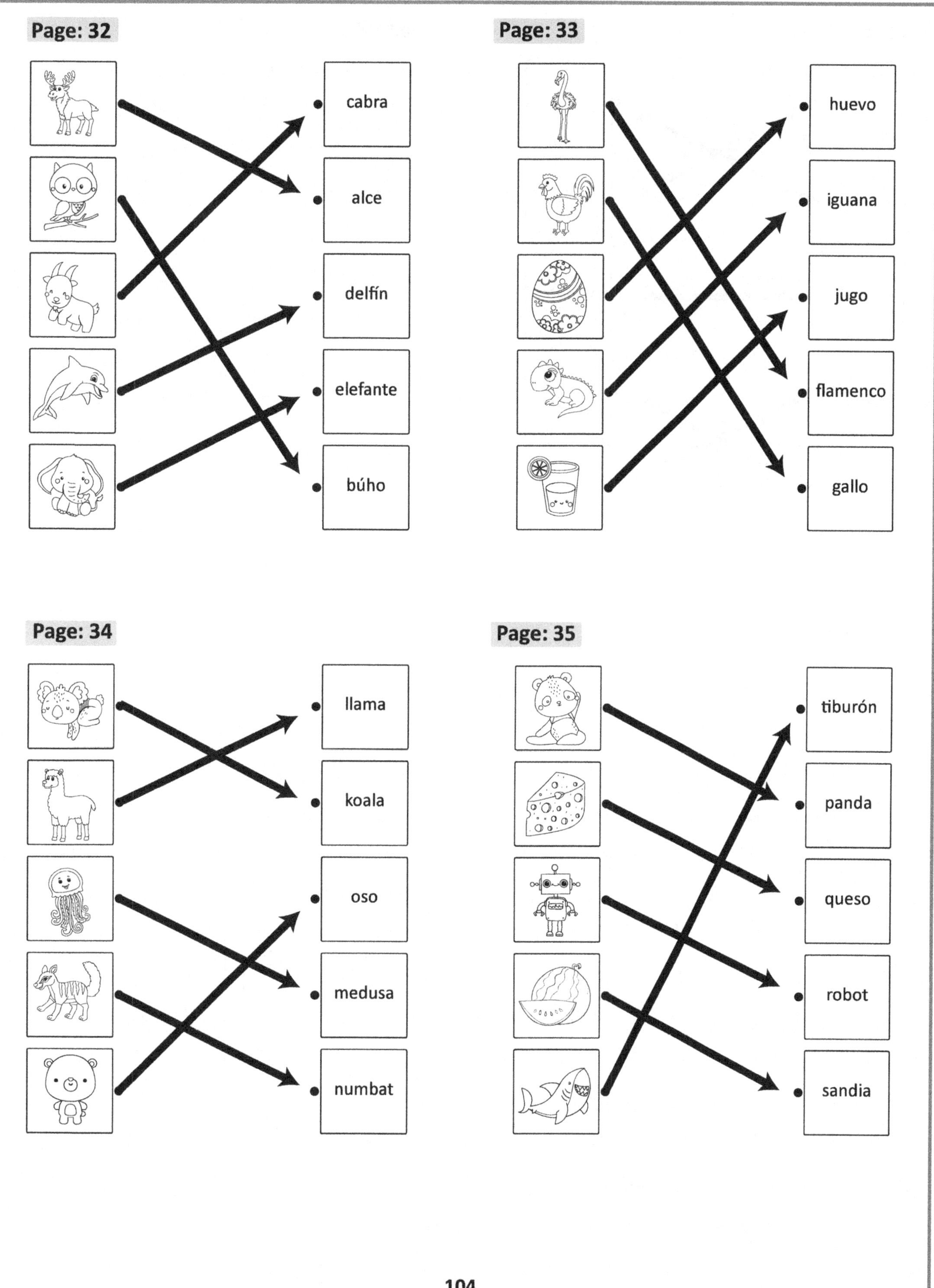
Page: 32
cabra
alce
delfín
elefante
búho
Page: 33
huevo
iguana
jugo
flamenco
gallo
Page: 34
llama
koala
oso
medusa
numbat
Page: 35
tiburón
panda
queso
robot
sandia

Page: 36

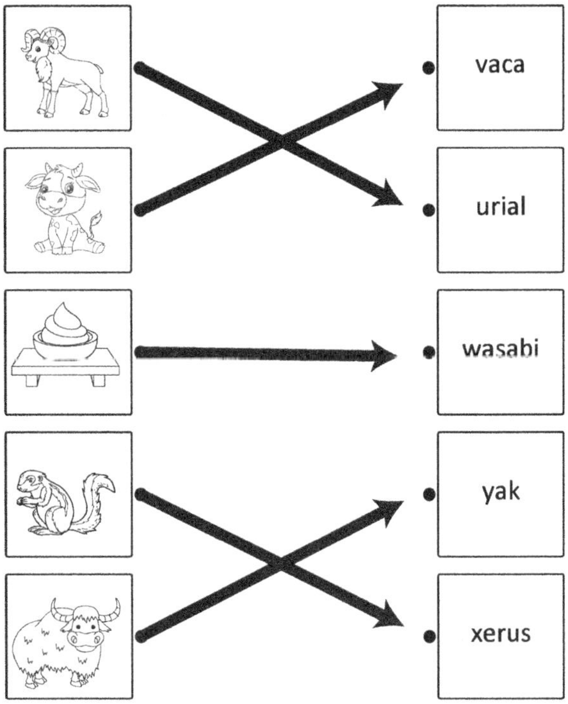

(urial picture)	→	vaca
(cow picture)	→	urial
(wasabi picture)	→	wasabi
(xerus picture)	→	yak
(yak picture)	→	xerus

Page: 59

a) Fill in the missing numbers/Rellenar los números que faltan.

1	2	3	4	5	6	7	8	9	10

b) Fill in the missing numbers/Rellenar los números que faltan.

11	12	13	14	15	16	17	18	19	20

c) Fill in the missing numbers/Rellenar los números que faltan.

21	22	23	24	25	26	27	28	29	30

d) Fill in the missing numbers/Rellenar los números que faltan.

31	32	33	34	35	36	37	38	39	40

e) Fill in the missing numbers/Rellenar los números que faltan.

41	42	43	44	45	46	47	48	49	50

Page: 60

a) Fill in the missing numbers/Rellenar los números que faltan.

51	52	53	54	55	56	57	58	59	60

b) Fill in the missing numbers/Rellenar los números que faltan.

61	62	63	64	65	66	67	68	69	70

c) Fill in the missing numbers/Rellenar los números que faltan.

71	72	73	74	75	76	77	78	79	80

d) Fill in the missing numbers/Rellenar los números que faltan.

81	82	83	84	85	86	87	88	89	90

e) Fill in the missing numbers/Rellenar los números que faltan.

91	92	93	94	95	96	97	98	99	100

Page: 61

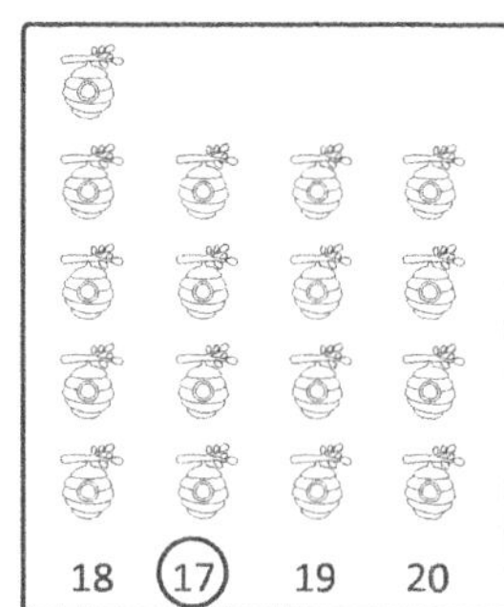

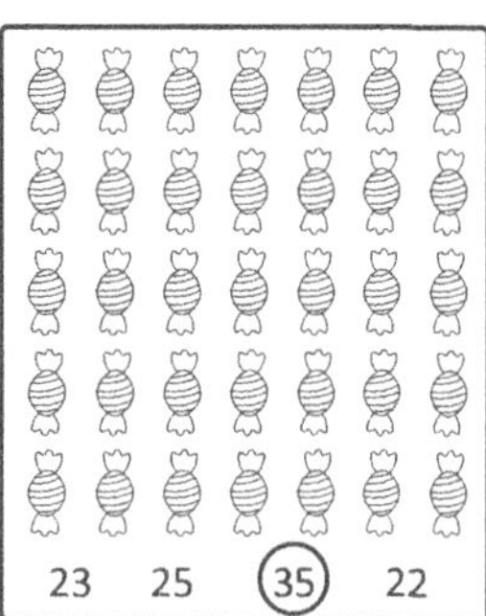

Page: 62

a) I see ..30.. pencils/Veo......30......lápices.

b) I see ..50.. pencils/Veo......50......lápices.

c) I see ..40.. pencils/Veo......40......lápices.

d) I see 70..... pencils/Veo......70......lápices.

e) I see ..80.. pencils/Veo......80......lápices.

f) I see ..60.. pencils/Veo......60......lápices.

g) I see ..100 pencils/Veo......100......lápices.

h) I see 90..... pencils/Veo......90......lápices.

Page: 74

Page: 75

Estrella

Corazón

Pentágono

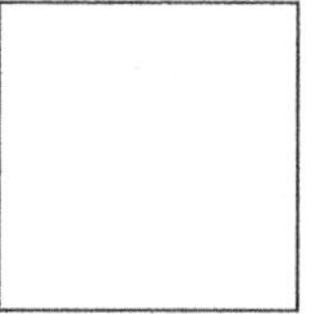

Cuadrado

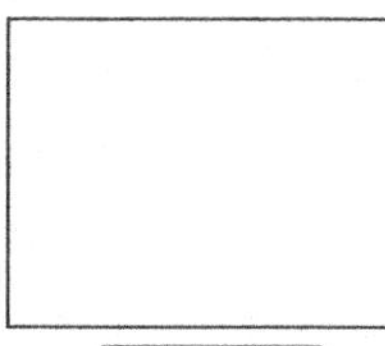

Rectángulo

Triángulo

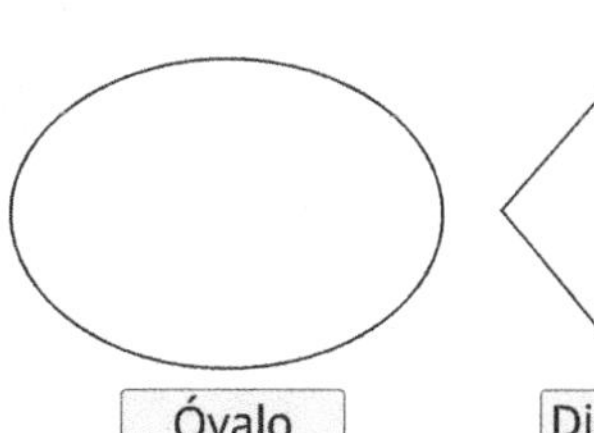

Círculo

Óvalo

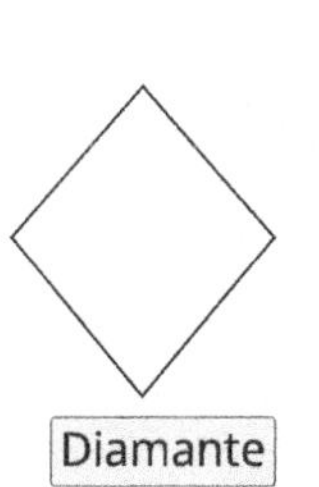

Diamante

Page: 76

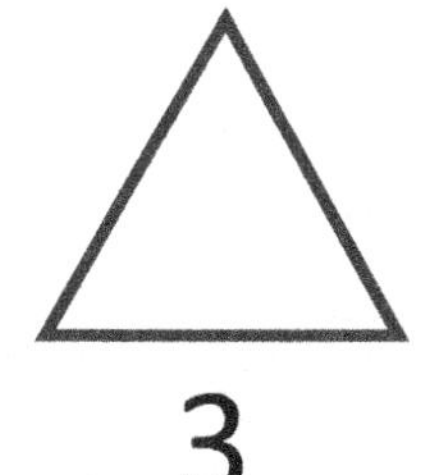

3

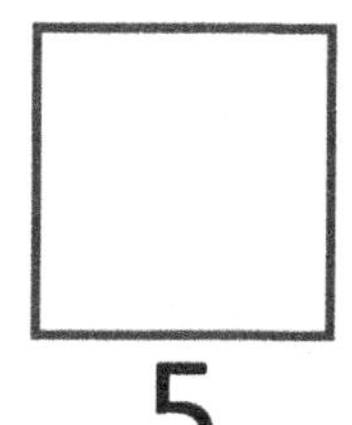

5

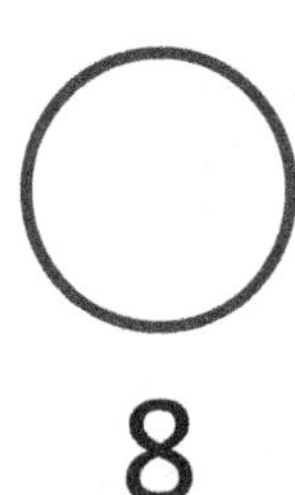

8

1

Page: 78

	English	Spanish	
1)	car	hcoce	coche
2)	bus	asbútuo	autobús
3)	train	etnr	tren
4)	bicycle	tbaiieclc	bicicleta
5)	boat	raocb	barco
6)	plane	iaónv	avión
7)	helicopter	itceoólehrp	helicóptero
8)	motorcycle	coomticleat	motocicleta
9)	truck	anmció	camión
10)	ship	oacrb	barco
11)	submarine	orasuibmn	submarino
12)	balloon	loogb	globo
13)	skateboard	tpeanita	patineta
14)	jet	croorh	chorro
15)	tram	arníatv	tranvía

Page: 79

	English	Spanish	
1)	cow	vaac	vaca
2)	pig	rocde	cerdo
3)	chicken	lloop	pollo
4)	sheep	evjao	oveja
5)	goat	barac	cabra
6)	horse	ablalco	caballo
7)	duck	tpoa	pato
8)	turkey	vaop	pavo
9)	donkey	rurob	burro
10)	rabbit	coejon	conejo
11)	goose	ongas	ganso
12)	dog	rpero	perro
13)	cat	toag	gato
14)	goat	abcra	cabra
15)	llama	llaam	llama

Page: 80

	English	Spanish	
1)	lion	eónl	león
2)	tiger	iegrt	tigre
3)	elephant	enteafle	elefante
4)	giraffe	ijafar	jirafa
5)	monkey	nmoo	mono
6)	gorilla	grlaio	gorila
7)	zebra	cbrae	cebra
8)	hippo	hmooiptapó	hipopótamo
9)	crocodile	oioocldrc	cocodrilo
10)	jaguar	rjuaag	jaguar
11)	snake	entpesrie	serpiente
12)	panther	atarnpe	pantera
13)	parrot	loro	loro
14)	chimpanzee	acmhnépic	chimpancé
15)	rhinoceros	nooneecritr	rinoceronte

Page: 81

	English	Spanish	
1)	apple	znaanma	manzana
2)	banana	nolpaát	plátano
3)	orange	rnnajaa	naranja
4)	strawberry	esfar	fresa
5)	pineapple	pañi	piña
6)	mango	agmno	mango
7)	grape	avu	uva
8)	watermelon	ansdía	sandía
9)	peach	ócmeolnot	melocotón
10)	pear	prea	pera
11)	cherry	erczea	cereza
12)	lemon	óilnm	limón
13)	kiwi	wkii	kiwi
14)	blueberry	nroaáand	arándano
15)	raspberry	ameasubfr	frambuesa

Page: 82

	English	Spanish	
1)	backpack	omilcah	mochila
2)	notebook	rcenuoad	cuaderno
3)	pencil	lázip	lápiz
4)	pen	aumlp	pluma
5)	eraser	ooarrbdr	borrador
6)	ruler	realg	regla
7)	book	libor	libro
8)	calculator	oaarulcldca	calculadora
9)	marker	mcodrara	marcador
10)	glue	tegeoapmn	pegamento
11)	scissors	stairej	tijeras
12)	folder	eatrapc	carpeta
13)	highlighter	mdcoaarr	marcador
14)	pencil case	euehsct	estuche
15)	sharpener	sspncaauta	sacapuntas

Page: 83

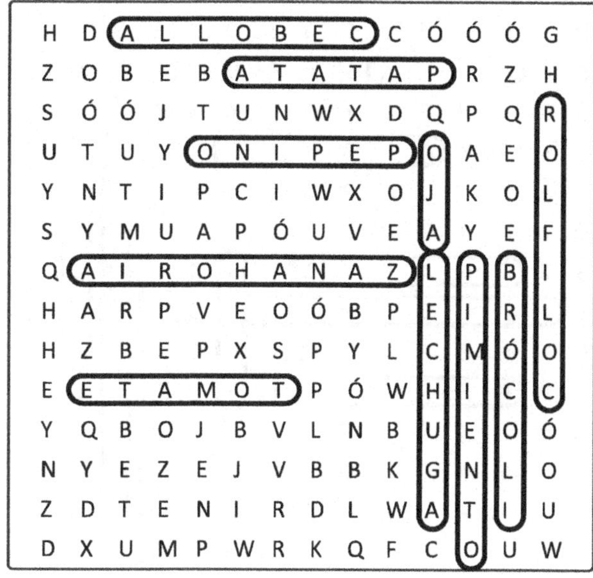

Page: 84

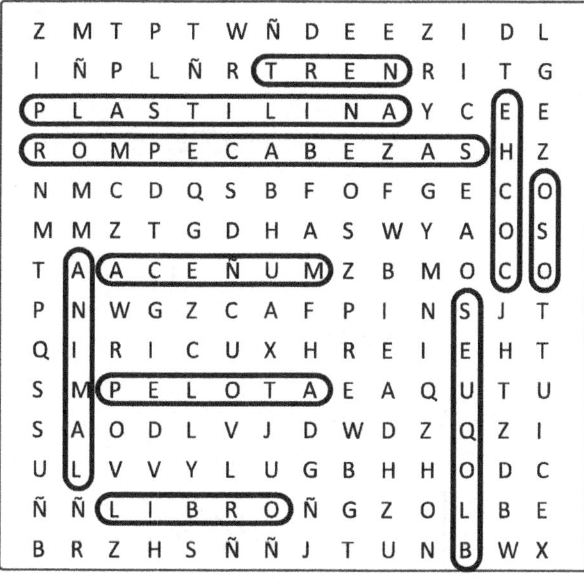

Page: 85

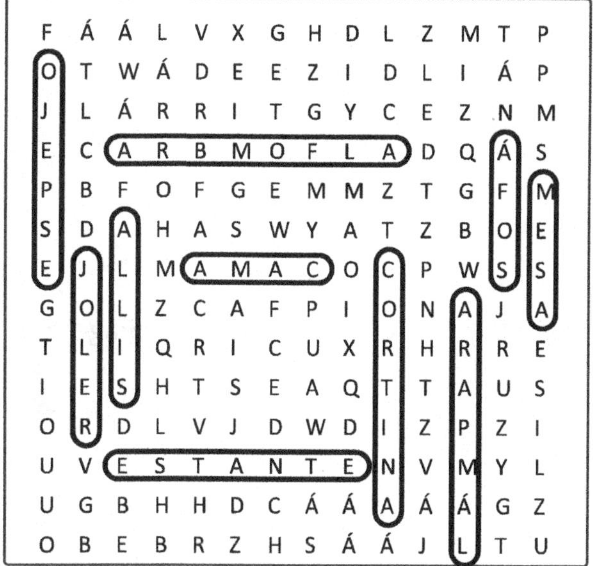

Page: 86

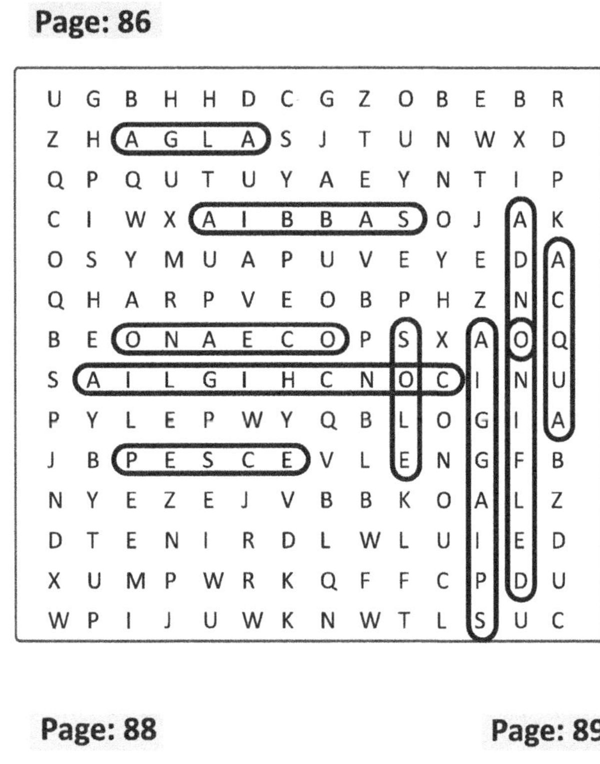

Page: 87

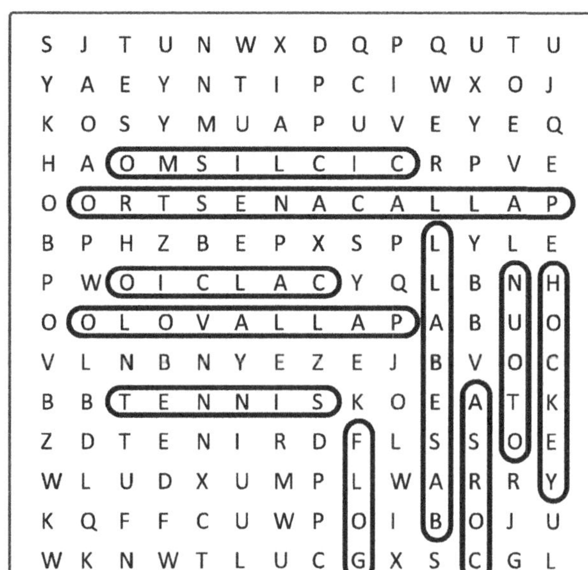

Page: 88

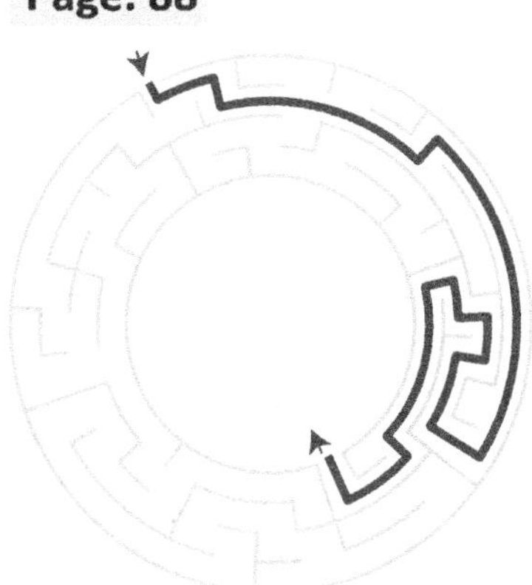

Page: 89

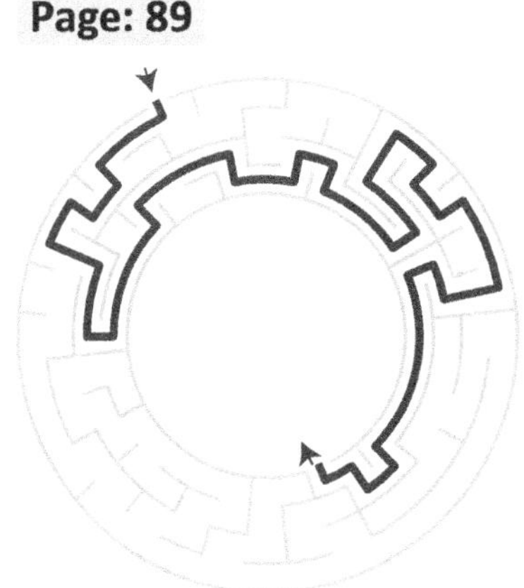

Page: 90

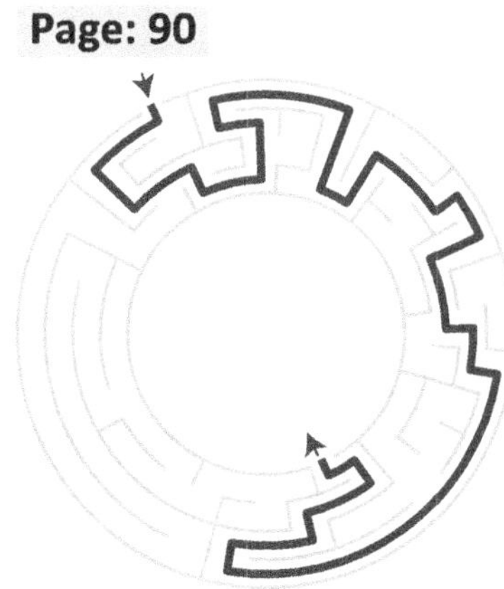

Page: 91

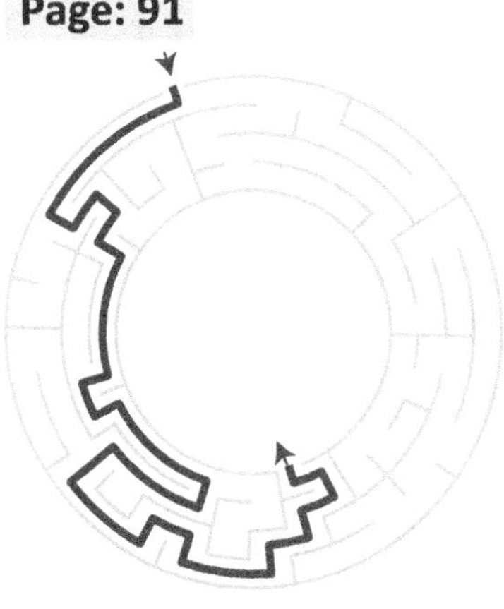

Page: 92

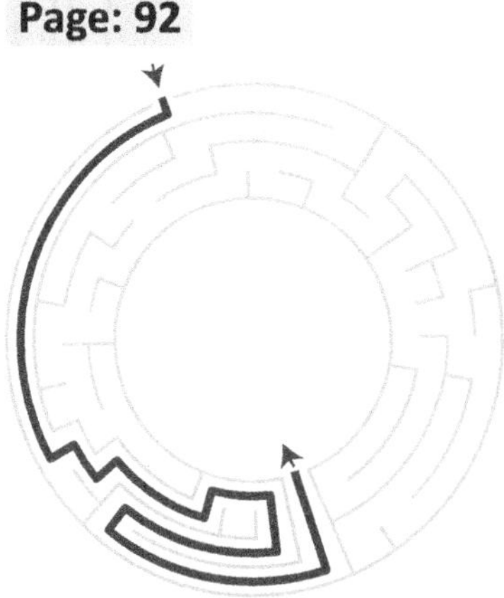

Page: 93

Page: 94

Page: 95

Page: 96

Page: 97

Page: 98	Page: 99	Page: 100	Page: 101	Page: 102
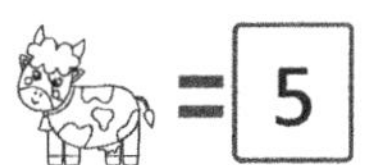 = 5	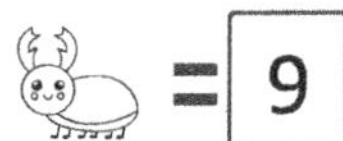 = 9	= 9	= 9	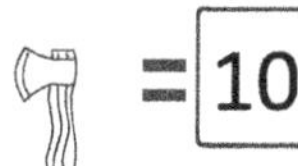 = 10
= 7	= 5	= 7	= 8	= 9
= 3	= 4	= 6	= 7	= 8
= 6	= 8	= 8	= 6	= 12
= 2	= 3	= 5	= 10	= 9
= 1	= 3	= 5	= 8	= 8

CERTIFICADO

DE LOGROS

Otorgado a

....

por su excelencia en

Mi primer libro de actividades bilingüe

....

....

Fecha Firma

Made in the USA
Las Vegas, NV
19 June 2024

91252807R00063